GREAT EVENTS
IN THE LIFE OF
LOUIS PASTEUR

Discovers that germs are carried
in the air, 1864

Saves the sick silkworms of France,
1865

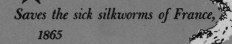

Saves the sheep and cattle which
are dying of anthrax, 1879

Inoculates Joseph Meister, who has
been bitten by a mad dog, 1885

*As long as Louis could study, he did
not feel homesick*

THE STORY OF
Louis Pasteur

By ALIDA SIMS MALKUS

Illustrated by JO SPIER

ENID LAMONTE MEADOWCROFT
Supervising Editor

PUBLISHERS Grosset & Dunlap NEW YORK

PRINTED IN THE UNITED STATES OF AMERICA

Library of Congress Catalog Card No. 52-11075

To
DAVID and STEVEN

Contents

CONTENTS

Illustrations

THE STORY OF
Louis Pasteur

Louis was more interested in the
pebbles than in the fish

CHAPTER ONE

The Tanner's Son

LOUIS, my son, come straight home after school," Jean Joseph Pasteur called from the doorway. "You and your friends must play here by the river."

Louis Pasteur stopped halfway down the garden path. "But Papa," he cried, "we were going into the hills exploring."

Louis was not very tall, but after all he *was* nine years old. "I can be trusted, Papa," he said.

"But no. It is not that," his father replied. "I shall have to tell you, my son—the wolves have come down from the hills. Yes, a great gray wolf has been seen. And not very far from town."

"Ooh!" Louis's gray eyes looked as round as marbles. "Very well, Papa. But of course," he answered.

A wolf! The very word was enough to frighten one. Louis remembered when he was just a little fellow, five years old. They had lived in Marnoz then. A mad dog had run through the village, biting everyone it met. And three people had died from the bites.

"A mad wolf is even worse than a mad dog, isn't it, Papa?" Louis said. He walked back up the path towards his father.

"Yes, it is." His father nodded solemnly. "Better hurry on to school now, son."

Louis turned and ran along the road into town. The Pasteur home was on the edge of the village of Arbois. This lovely little town was in the heart of France. Arbois nestled among the foothills of the Jura Mountains. And in the year 1829, there were many wolves in those mountains.

Louis ran all the way to school. He ran more

swiftly than usual, and he could run very fast. He was slender, but he was wiry. Now he was imagining that a wolf was right at his heels.

When school was over that day Louis talked with his friends about the wolf. They were frightened and excited.

"My father says that no one must leave his house after dark," cried Jules Vercel. Jules was Louis's best friend. He was a chubby, dark-haired boy.

"Well, I'm not afraid," boasted a new boy named Charles. "I'll carry a big stick." Charles was a tall, blonde boy, eleven years old. Now he pretended to swing a stick at an imaginary wolf.

"Foolish boy, not even a man can always beat off a mad wolf," said Pierre Coulon, another of Louis's friends.

"Let's go to my house to play," Louis said.

"Yes, let's," Pierre agreed. "It's great fun to play there."

The four boys scampered along the Rue Courcelles towards the Pasteur home.

"Is your father going to tan hides today?" asked Jules.

"Yes," Louis called over his shoulder as he ran ahead. "Nicole, the herdsman, brought some fresh sheepskins down from the hills today. If we hurry, Papa may let us help tan them."

"Do you know how to make leather?" asked the new boy in surprise.

"I'm learning," Louis replied as he slowed down to a walk. "You see, my father, my grandfather, and his father before him, were all tanners."

"I love to play in the tannery yard," cried Jules. "But don't fall into the tanning pits, you boys."

"I should say not!" Louis laughed. "We'd get the hide and hair both taken right off us. There's strong acid in those pits. Look, Charles, there's the tannery up ahead."

The Pasteurs lived in a two-story stone house built right on the edge of the pretty Cuisance River. The road from Arbois ran past the house, over the Cuisance bridge, and on to the next town.

"We always live beside a river," Louis explained to the new boy. "A tanner must have lots of water."

Just below the bridge there was a dam. It made a pretty waterfall. Above the falls there were deep green pools where brook trout darted in and out of the golden shallows.

Louis's mother was waiting at the gate. She had been looking anxiously up the road, shading her eyes with her hand. Mama Etienette was a rosy, plump woman. Now she smiled with relief.

"Well, so here you are, boys!" she exclaimed. "I've been worried about you because of the wolf. Come in." She held the gate open for them and bent to kiss Louis.

The Pasteur family lived on the second floor of the stone house. A workshop filled the first floor. Louis led the boys through the shop and out into the back yard.

His father was working over the tanning pits, beside the river. He was pushing the hides under the dark tanning fluid with a pole, but he looked up as the boys appeared.

"Welcome, lads," he called cheerfully. "Don't get too near the pits."

Piles of salted hides and mounds of different kinds of bark stood beside the pits.

"What a terrible smell!" said Charles, holding his nose. Pierre held his nose, too.

"I love the smell," said Louis proudly. "It's not terrible. It's nice, once you're used to it. I hardly notice it. Well," he admitted, "maybe it is a little stronger than usual today. That smell comes from the raw hides and the tannic acid."

"Now I see why you have to live beside a river," cried Charles. "You must have water running right into the tanning pits. Let's go down to the river and see where it branches off."

The other boys were already standing on the bank. "Let's go fishing," said Jules.

"All right," replied Louis good-naturedly. "I'll get the net for you. I saw two trout in the pool just above the bridge."

"Which eye did you see them with?" teased Jules.

"With my farsighted eye, of course," laughed Louis. He got the net for Jules and they followed the other boys down to the river's edge.

"Louis can see things that nobody else can see at all," Jules told Charles.

Now, though Louis had gray eyes, one eye looked almost green. And it was true that with one eye he could see clearly things which were far off. And with the other eye he could see all kinds of tiny things.

He didn't mind being teased about it. Now,

as the boys began to wade along the river, he was more interested in the pebbles than in the fish.

"Look, look, Pierre!" he cried. "Here's a beauty! See the crystals in the center? Look closely."

"What makes crystals?" asked Pierre curiously.

"I don't know," replied Louis thoughtfully, "but some day I shall find out."

"Look, Louis, look!" shouted Charles just then. "Jules has caught two fish. Let's go farther up the stream. There will be more fish up in the hills." And he started off upstream.

"No, no!" Louis called after him. "Don't go into the hills, Charles. Have you forgotten already? Wolves are abroad."

"Who's afraid of wolves?" cried Charles. And he ran up the riverbank laughing.

"Come back, come back," Louis shouted.

"Oh, he's only going a little way," said Jules. "He's just trying to scare us. We'd better go back. I heard your mother calling."

"I heard her too," Louis said, "but I did want to hunt for more crystals. I guess Charles would not be foolish enough to go far. Well, I suppose we must go home."

His mother met the boys at the back door. Her tender face was anxious. "Louis, my child, what took you so long?" she said. "I want you to carry a message in to town to Dr. Dumont. Say that little Émilie is not well, and ask him if he will come."

She straightened Louis's collar and smoothed his hair. "I am worried about your baby sister," she went on. "There has been something wrong with poor little Émilie ever since that dreadful time when she was so sick last year. And the good God takes so many babies! Perhaps it was the milk that made Émilie sick. Even the calves died last year."

Now why should that be, Louis thought, as he ran down the road back into town, with Jules and Pierre close behind him.

Louis left the message for the doctor. Then the boys turned towards the square. There was a crowd in front of the blacksmith shop.

[*11*]

The boys hurried over to find out what was happening.

"Nicole has been bitten," said one of the men in the crowd. "The wolf sprang out on him from the woods. Nicole beat it off with a club, but it tore his leg badly."

The boys squirmed their way in between the grownups until they could see. The smith stood at his forge heating a poker in the glow-

ing coals. On a bench sprawled Nicole, with his leg stuck out straight before him. It was frightfully torn and bleeding.

"A pity," said one man. "They will have to burn the poison out. And his leg will probably never be any good again."

"It's better for him to have a useless leg than to lose his life," said another man. "Burning out the poison is the only way to cure him."

Poor Nicole! Louis was horrified by what had happened to him, but he could not turn his eyes away. The smith pulled his poker from the coals and thrust the white-hot metal into Nicole's wounds.

A cry of pain burst from the herdsman. Two men had to hold him. It was terrible. Wasn't there some other way to save him? Louis felt that he would never forget that cry.

"And Nicole had just finished selling his hides," said the blacksmith. "He was on his way back up into the hills by the river road."

Then suddenly Louis remembered something. Charles! What had happened to Charles? He had gone up the river towards the

[*13*]

hills. Louis broke from the crowd and ran all the way home.

He was out of breath when he reached the gate. Virginie, his older sister, was standing there waiting for him.

"Did you see Charles, the new boy?" he panted.

No, Virginie had not seen him. "Did you see Charles again, Papa?" cried Louis as his father came to the door.

But no, no one had seen the new boy. Now Louis told how the wolf had attacked Nicole.

"What if Charles did go on up the river road, Papa?" Louis asked fearfully.

"We must take our guns and set out at once to look for him," replied his father gravely. "But first we'll find out if the lad has returned home. We must hurry. It's getting dark."

CHAPTER TWO

The Mad Wolf of Arbois

HERE comes Dr. Dumont," called Virginie from the gate. "He knows everyone; perhaps he has heard something."

"Doctor, Doctor," cried Louis before the doctor could pull up his horse and stop his buggy. "Have you seen Charles? We are afraid —the wolf—"

"Yes," said the doctor. "I saw Charles crossing the fields, coming up from the river. He was walking slowly, but he must be safely home by now."

"Good! Has the wolf been found?" Louis asked. "The wolf that bit Nicole?"

"No," the doctor replied, "and I am told that seven people have been bitten."

[*15*]

He went into the house to see little Émilie.

For a long time after this, everyone was fearful that the wolf might still be about. The children of Arbois had to play near home. Louis and Jules played in the tannery yard,

and Pierre often joined them. But Charles was kept at home to punish him for having stayed out until dusk.

The tannery was a delightful place to play in. The floors of the workshop were covered with scraps of leather from which wonderful things could be made. One day Louis made a bag for Virginie, who had given him some crayons. Pierre made a dog collar. And Jules made a slingshot.

"Jules, you shouldn't make a slingshot," Louis said. "It's cruel to kill birds and squirrels. And what else is it good for?"

"Well, you never can tell," said Jules. "I can just practice with it. Some day I'd like to pepper that old General Delort who rides across the bridge every day, all dressed up in his fancy uniform. I'd just use pebbles, of course."

"I know," agreed Louis. "General Delort thinks he owns Arbois. He never notices us."

The boys had just finished their leather work when Louis's father appeared in the doorway. "You boys can help me today," he said. "We'll begin by washing the new hides. Later I'll scrape them."

Louis threw the stiff salty hides into the washing pit, where the clear water from the river flowed over them. Pierre and Jules helped.

[*17*]

"They have to soak a long time before they are ready for the acid pit," said Louis's father. "Stand back now, boys. I'm going to lift some hides out of the acid. Be careful it does not splash on you. Acid burns!"

"Could we scrape the hides?" cried Pierre. He was so interested in the work that he forgot to hold his nose because of the smell.

"See," Louis laughed in delight. "I told you one gets used to it. I wish Charles were here. But he wasn't even at school today."

"It's too hard for you boys to scrape skins," said Louis's father. "But you can stir up the tannic acid pit, so the dye doesn't settle."

"What's the tannin for, Papa?" Louis asked, "and what does it do to the hides, and why?"

"Such a boy for questions!" said his father proudly. "The acid softens the stiff hides and loosens the hair so it can be scraped off. And the tannin tans them, and preserves them. It keeps them from getting brittle and cracking. Why, I don't know."

"Well, I'd like to know why," Louis persisted, as he and the boys stirred up the tannin pit. "And some day I'm going to find out."

"Are you going to be a tanner too, Louis?" asked Jules. "My father says that only the sons of tanners become tanners when they grow up, because they are used to the smell!"

"No, I shall not be a tanner," Louis said. "I want to study and be a Monitor at school. And then I want to be a teacher some day."

"But Louis, you are the youngest and the smallest boy in the class," said Jules. "And you know that only the older boys are chosen to be Monitors. A Monitor has to know a lot to teach the younger ones. He has to read all the lessons aloud, very well and very clearly."

Yes, Louis knew all that. But still he did want to be a Monitor.

"I shall learn to read as well, or even better, than the older boys," Louis said to himself as he went to bed that night. "Charles is a very good reader, because he is nearly twelve. Perhaps he will help me if he is back in school tomorrow."

But the next day Charles was again absent from school. And the day following, his seat was still empty. Monsieur Romanet told the boys that Charles was very ill. Then suddenly the boys heard that Charles had died.

"It was because of the wolf," said Monsieur Romanet sadly.

"The wolf bit Charles, just as it bit Nicole," Louis said to his mother that night. "It was only a little bite, and Charles didn't tell his mother about it until he had a fever. And she called Dr. Dumont. Why does a wolf bite kill one, Mama?"

"It puts a poison into the blood, my son," replied his mother. "We know no cure, alas. The only thing that can be done is to burn the poison away at once."

"But why does the poison not kill at once,

Mama?" Louis asked earnestly. "The tanning acids are poison and they would kill at once."

"I do not know, my son." Etienette patted

his head and turned to her stove, where the supper stew was simmering. "It must be that with time the poison grows stronger," she added.

She did not like to talk of a thing so sad. But Louis could not forget it. He puzzled over what his mother had said: "With time the poison grows stronger."

"Grows?" he thought. "How can a poison grow? Only living things grow, do they not?

Is the poison alive then?" he asked himself. He thought about this for a long time. But he had many other things to think about too. He loved his school, and tried more and more earnestly to do well in his lessons. He learned slowly because he thought a great deal about each thing that he learned.

"I do so want to be a Monitor," Louis said to his father one evening. "I am twelve now. But I am still the smallest boy in the class, Papa, and the others are always chosen first."

"Perhaps you will be chosen some day, if you study hard," replied his father encouragingly. "You will have to know more than the others. Come. I will help you."

So night after night Louis and Papa bent over the lesson books at one end of the long table. Mama folded back the red-checked cloth the moment supper was over, and drew the oil lamp closer.

She hustled the two little girls off to bed, while Virginie, now quite a young lady at sixteen, embroidered linen for her marriage chest. And all was busy in the warm kitchen and living room of the happy Pasteur family.

Louis paid close attention to his lessons, too.

But months passed, and not once did Monsieur Romanet choose him to be a Monitor.

At last one day Madame Pasteur decided that she must find out how Louis was getting on at school. She put on her best bonnet and shawl and went to see the schoolmaster. "Do you think that our Louis is so slow at learning, then, Monsieur?" she asked anxiously.

"We-ell, it might seem so," replied Monsieur Romanet thoughtfully. "But that is only because Louis takes the time to understand. And he remembers. Others may learn more quickly, and forget just as quickly. Pouf, it is

[23]

gone, like that!" And he snapped his fingers.

"Louis never says anything that he is not sure of," added Monsieur Romanet. "And what an eye he has to observe!"

"Yes, already he paints most beautifully," said Madame Pasteur proudly, "as you know."

"He does indeed," agreed the schoolmaster, "but somehow I think that it will not be for painting that he will be remembered."

"Remembered?" Louis's mother could hardly believe her ears. "Do you mean you

think our Louis will some day be famous?"

"I do indeed," said Monsieur Romanet. "He will be a great man some day. Mark my words. He may even teach in a great university."

When Louis's mother returned home she told Papa and Louis that Monsieur Romanet was very much pleased with Louis's schoolwork.

Louis was very happy to hear this. Now he would no longer be shy about asking the schoolmaster questions. There were some things which had puzzled him for a long time.

The next day after school Louis asked Monsieur Romanet, "What are acids, Monsieur, if you please? And how can something that is not alive—like sickness—grow?"

"Those are very good questions, Louis," replied his teacher. "We do not know why sickness grows worse. But we do know that acids are chemicals. They are not alive as we are. And yet they do actually grow—like crystals. You will learn about this when you study chemistry."

"Chemistry," repeated Louis, his eyes shining. "That is what I shall study when I am old enough."

He looked out of the window at the square of Arbois. He could just see the blacksmith shop. And he remembered that day so long ago when Nicole had had his wounds burned out. Nicole had lived, it was true, but he had limped badly ever since.

"And poisons, Monsieur Romanet," Louis asked, thinking of the wolf, "are they chemicals also?"

"Yes," nodded the schoolmaster, "but very little is known of them."

"Then poisons could grow, too," Louis said slowly. Yes, his mother had said something like that long ago, when poor Charles died.

"Some day," Louis said, "perhaps I can find a way to stop poisons from growing. If I can—" He did not finish his sentence for just then a roll of drums sounded across the square.

Rat-tat-a-tat, rat-tat-a-tat, boom-de-de-boom, boom, boom!

"What is it?" Louis cried. He seized his cap

[26]

and little knapsack, and in three seconds was running out of the door, followed by Monsieur Romanet.

"The Hôtel de ville, the City Hall!" exclaimed the schoolmaster. "Look, the citizens are arming! Can it be—war?"

CHAPTER THREE

Louis and Jules Defend the Bridge

PEOPLE were running towards the City Hall. In front of that building a company of Arbois citizens was drawn up, armed with guns, and dressed in soldiers' uniforms.

"Arbois is rising to the defense of liberty," cried a man in captain's uniform, who was giving out guns to the men in the crowd. "Long live Liberty!"

"*Vive la Liberté!*" The cry echoed across the square and down the streets of Arbois.

Boom-de-de-boom, the drums rolled, and Louis's heart beat *boom-de-de-boom* against his chest.

"Why are we fighting?" he cried to one man and then to another. But suddenly he remem-

"Long live Liberty!" the cry echoed

bered. Papa had told him that there might be trouble here in Arbois.

"You know, France is ruled by the King," Papa had said. "But for some time the people of France have had the right to elect men to help govern the country. We have the right also to say what we think, and print it in newspapers. This is called 'freedom of speech.' But now the King wants to take these rights from us."

"And what will the people do then?" Louis had asked.

"We'll rise up in arms against such a thing," Papa had said grimly. "We'll form a free state."

Well, now the trouble had started. Papa must surely know about it. But where was he?

"Have you seen my father? Is he here?" cried Louis, running from one man to another.

"Jean Joseph Pasteur?" a citizen soldier replied at last. "He's already guarding the bridge! The King's troops are marching on Arbois. They are coming from Poligny. But we'll stop them! *Vive la Liberté!*"

So Papa was guarding the bridge right beside their home! And the soldiers must cross that bridge in order to enter Arbois. Anything might happen. The family might be shot!

Never had Louis run faster than he ran then along the Rue Courcelles towards home. He splashed through the little pools of April rain lying on the road like bits of blue sky.

[*31*]

There ahead was the tannery. And there was Papa on the far side of the bridge. He had placed a company of men right across the road, blocking the bridge.

"Papa, Papa!" Louis fairly flew across the bridge and up to his father. "It is true then? The Royalists are marching on Arbois?"

"Yes, yes, my son." Jean Joseph Pasteur laid a hand on Louis's shoulder. "Run back to the house, quick! Take care of Mama and your sisters."

As he spoke the road shook with the tramp of feet and the clatter of hoofs. Back to the tannery raced Louis. His mother and the girls were looking out of an upstairs window. Dark-haired Josephine stood between Virginie and little Émilie.

"I shall stay at the gate, Mama," Louis shouted.

Whatever happened, that was his place, he thought.

Boom-de-de-boom, boom, boom! Here they came! How could he help stop them? How could he defend his beloved Arbois? Never should a Royalist soldier march past this gate! But what weapons had he?

Boom-de-de-boom! Louis gave one look up the road and turned and ran into the house.

"Poor Louis! He's afraid, Mama," said Virginie, looking down from the window.

But a few moments later Louis reappeared lugging a great bucket of evil-smelling tanning acid. This would stop some of them!

Now who was that running along the road? He perched the bucket on the wall, ready to dump it.

[33]

"Louis, Louis!" cried a familiar voice.

It was Jules peering over the gate. He was panting, and his face was red. He had run all the way from town.

"Jules! I'm so glad it's you. Goodness, you spoke just in time," Louis said in a low voice. "Help me lift this bucket up onto the post."

· *Br-rroom, br-room,* the roll of enemy drums grew louder. The clanking of the gun carriages, the grating of wheels, the hoofbeats, drew nearer. The boys waited with thumping hearts.

"Atten-*shun,* soldiers of Arbois!" they could hear Louis's father shout suddenly to the men who were guarding the bridge. "They are here, the King's soldiers!"

And here they were! First came the light cavalry. After them trundled the guns. Next came two hundred grenadiers, marching ten abreast along the road. How tall they were; and taller because of their high, pointed helmets. Their red coats and high-buttoned leggings were magnificent. They quite outshone the faded old uniforms of Arbois.

"But wait till it comes to defending our city," said Louis fiercely, "and see who makes the bravest showing." He threw out his chest and clenched his fists.

Jules reached into his pocket and pulled out the slingshot which he had made so long ago. "See," he said in a whisper, "I knew it would be useful some day."

"Yes," Louis's eyes shone, "yes, this is the time, Jules."

The King's cavalry had spread out across the road, from the hedge of poplars on one side to the row of poplars on the other. The artillery pulled up into their midst. The grenadiers halted behind them, facing the bridge, which was guarded by Papa and his men.

The captain of cavalry rode forward. "What is the meaning of this?" he thundered. "Stand aside. Let us pass."

"Stay where you are," replied Jean Joseph Pasteur clearly and sternly. "We people of Arbois do not allow armed forces to enter our city."

[35]

"Stand aside, I say," shouted the captain angrily. "Arbois is against the King, and we are King's men. We have been sent to put down—"

But he did not finish; for at this moment Jules aimed his slingshot at the beautiful shiny flanks of the captain's gray horse.

Ping-g! The animal reared and snorted and wheeled around in circles. The captain was kept so busy handling him that he could say nothing more for some minutes.

When he had the horse under control once more, he began again. "We have been sent to punish the rebels of Arbois. Who is the leader of this riot?" He looked fiercely at Jean Joseph Pasteur.

There was a moment of complete silence. Then a shout went up from the men of Arbois who had come to defend the bridge. "We are all leaders," they cried. "We all stand for freedom."

The gunners sprang to their guns. Louis stood up on the wall, with the bucket of tanning acid beside him. Would the captain give the order to fire on the men of Arbois?

"Oh, where are the rest of our soldiers?" Louis thought wildly. "Why don't they come to help defend the bridge?"

The cavalry captain was riding back and forth speaking to his men.

"Shoot him again, Jules," said Louis firmly.

Jules fitted a stone into a sling, but at that very moment they heard the tramp of feet along the Rue Courcelles. The rest of Arbois's citizens were coming at last—every man who could carry a gun.

The Mayor of Arbois was leading them. Beside him rode the General Baron Delort, his chest covered with his decorations and medals.

"He thinks he's the most important person in Arbois," said Jules, "because he's a baron."

"But he's a Royalist," cried Louis. "He's not for Free France. He's for the King."

Now the cavalry captain spoke to Jean Joseph Pasteur again. "I order you to let me cross this bridge," he said. "I wish to go on to the City Hall to speak to your Mayor."

"That will not be necessary," replied Jean Joseph Pasteur. "The Mayor is coming now with all the men of Arbois."

Suddenly the General Baron Delort galloped ahead of the Mayor. He clattered across the bridge, reined in his horse, and held up his hand.

"He's a King's man," Jules muttered.

"Let me have your sling, Jules." Louis's eyes flashed as he reached for the slingshot. He took aim.

"At this historic moment," the baron began to speak, "I feel that it is fitting that I—"

Ping-g! The sharp stone struck the baron's horse in the rump. The horse rose up and pawed the air. Then it came down with a jolt. Before the baron could get the animal under control another stone struck it in the flank. This was too much for the high-spirited horse.

[39]

It bolted away up the road, quite out of control, and disappeared in the distance. And the baron was not seen on the streets for a week.

Louis almost fell off the wall in his excitement. Jules did fall off, and rolled on the ground with laughter.

But Louis was looking to see of what further help he could be. He could not aim at the captain again without hitting the Mayor. This brave gentleman had ridden forward and was addressing the captain.

"We shall defend our rights to the last man," cried the Mayor, and trotted quickly back to his men.

The captain of cavalry whipped out his sword and opened his mouth to shout a command. But suddenly his horse whirled around and bolted. The soldiers parted, and right through the lines went the captain!

There was a roll of drums. "About-*face!*" shouted the first lieutenant. For the captain had disappeared, and after all, there were twice as many Free French as there were Royalists.

Then the cavalry, and the two hundred grenadiers, and the artillery, all began moving. And they went marching back down the road in the direction from which they had come. A great shout went up from the men of Arbois, and Louis and Jules shouted, too.

"We shall always fight for freedom, eh, Jules?" cried Louis, jumping down from the wall. They shook hands and embraced each other joyfully.

That night the Pasteur family sat at supper talking over the exciting events of the day.

"Of course," Papa said, "it was good that we were able to keep the Royalists from crossing the bridge until our own soldiers got there."

"Yes, was it not?" said Mama Etienette, her eyes sparkling. She shook her head at Virginie and Josephine and laid a finger across her lips.

"We were watching from the window. I told Louis he might wait at the gate; but I kept my eye on him and Jules all the time," she added, smiling merrily at Louis.

[41]

"I wonder what happened to Baron De-lort," said Dr. Dumont, who had just dropped in to talk things over with his good friend Jean Joseph Pasteur.

"He is such a fine horseman, yet he could not control his horse," nodded Papa, his eyes twinkling.

"And the captain of cavalry," the good doctor went on, "his departure was most surprising."

"Well, we could not let our freedom be taken away," said Papa heartily, "could we, my son?"

"Long live Liberty!" cried Louis.

CHAPTER FOUR

An Exciting Journey

I SHALL cream these mushrooms you gathered, Josephine," said Mama Etienette. She poured a cup of thick yellow cream over the golden-brown slices which were simmering in butter.

"M'm, delicious!" Louis sniffed, as he came in from school and set down his books. "What else for supper, Mama?"

"Your nose should tell you," laughed Mama. She stooped to open the oven. A warm fragrance filled the air as she pulled out six long loaves of French bread.

Then she set some pewter plates on the table.

"Come now, we are having supper early," she called.

No sooner was the family seated than there came a knock on the door. Louis jumped up to open it.

"Monsieur Romanet!" he exclaimed in surprise. There stood the schoolmaster, his hat in his hand.

"Come in, come in, Monsieur," Papa called out. "Virginie will set another place at the table."

The kitchen was bright with sunshine. The plastered walls and beamed ceiling looked down upon a merry feast.

Mama Etienette thanked her stars that there was a good dinner. Creamed mushrooms, potato soufflé, eggplant baked whole with garlic, the warm fresh bread, and jelly from the wonderful purple grapes of Arbois.

Monsieur Romanet said he had no idea that it was so near dinnertime! He had come to talk to Monsieur Pasteur on a matter of some importance.

"It is about Louis," he said, as he picked up

[*44*]

his fork. "I feel sure that he will make a fine teacher."

Mama and Papa smiled in delight.

"But I feel that he needs more schooling than he can get here in Arbois," Monsieur Romanet went on. "Louis should go to Paris to study. He is now fifteen, and he should begin to prepare for the Teachers College."

Louis go away to Paris? The family sat wide-eyed.

"But," said Louis's father, "Louis is very young yet. Where could he stay? Who would look after him? He cannot live alone."

"I know just the place," said the schoolmaster. "The Barbet School. It is very good, and it will take Louis, I am sure."

"But," said Papa Jean Joseph, "will that not cost a great deal? We are not rich people, Monsieur."

"Monsieur Barbet is a Free French, and will take Louis for a small sum," replied the schoolmaster.

They could talk no more for the moment, for now Mama served the final treat—the dessert. Delicious raspberry tarts, topped with whipped cream!

When the meal was over Monsieur Romanet took up his hat and stick. Papa went with him down to the gate. When he came back he said, "Well, Louis is to go to Paris to school."

Ah, what excitement there was at this! Louis could scarcely believe it. He was delighted when he heard that Jules was to go too. Jules was such fun.

"What shall I pack my clothes in?" asked Louis. "I must begin to get my things ready."

But many weeks must pass before it would be time to go. Louis and Jules talked and thought about their journey constantly.

At last the day of their departure came. It was a cold, rainy morning in late October. The Pasteurs rose in the dark, chilly hour before dawn. After a hot breakfast they climbed into the wagon and drove along the muddy road into Arbois. The coach for Paris was waiting in the courtyard of the inn of Arbois.

"Just think," cried Papa, as he pulled up his horses before the inn, "in forty-eight hours you will be in Paris, my son. A wonderful opportunity! You will study your best, eh?"

"Yes, Papa. I shall study hard, of course!"

Though he spoke bravely, Louis's heart was heavy. How could he bear to go away from home for so long? But there was the coach! The passengers were already climbing in. The five horses were being hitched up by the glimmering lantern light. The baggage was being strapped on behind.

Louis kissed each one of his family fondly. He tried to blink back the tears in his eyes. Suddenly he felt that he could not bear to leave. He had never been parted from his family for a day in his life.

Even the merry Jules was sad. It was hard to go away from home for the first time.

"You will write to us often, Louis?" Mama Etienette asked, throwing her arms around him once more.

"Yes, Mama, I will write." For the twentieth time they embraced.

Now there was no room left inside the coach. The boys had to climb up to the top seat, behind the driver. The seat was covered only by a leaky canvas tarpaulin.

The rain had now turned to sleet. The coach started up. The wheels jolted over the cobblestones.

"Good-by, good-by," Louis and Jules called. They waved from their swaying perch until the faces of their families disappeared in the darkness.

The sleet stung Louis's face as he leaned forward for one last glimpse of Arbois. The coach rolled down the dark street. It passed the tannery, it clattered across the bridge. They were on their way to Paris.

For a long time neither of the boys spoke. Then Jules said, laughing, "Well, at least up here we do not get mud splashed in our faces."

"How far have we come, do you think, Jules?" Louis asked. "It's two hundred miles to Paris." It seemed to him that they had been traveling forever.

But Jules was having a wonderful time.

"Think of all the wonderful things we're going to see," he reminded Louis. "Palaces, and gardens with fountains, like in fairy tales. And famous waxworks—" Jules stopped, out of breath.

Now the sun came out, and they were passing through the most beautiful vineyards of France. They rumbled through little villages, past beautiful châteaux and wonderful old castles.

Whenever the coach stopped to change horses the boys climbed down from their high seat and stretched their stiff legs. That night they stayed at a shabby old inn. They were almost too tired to eat, and were asleep the minute their heads touched the pillows. They did not even notice the hard bed nor the tiny room in which they slept.

All the next day, they went on and on. Towards evening the driver called out, "We sleep tonight at an inn where kings have slept."

"You see," Jules gloated.

"I know," Louis said with a laugh, "but I'd rather see the tannery by the Cuisance than the most wonderful inn in the whole world."

Finally the coach rolled to a stop before the inn where kings had slept. The boys were given a low-ceiled room in which King Louis XIII himself had spent the night.

"I don't care how many kings have slept here," Louis said as he tumbled into bed. "I wish I were in Arbois."

For a long time he could not sleep. He felt very sad and homesick. But the next morning the sun shone and he thought, "Paris will be wonderful, and then I shall not feel this way."

Past beautiful Fontainebleau rolled the coach the next day, on and on. Now at last they were entering Paris. Down dark and narrow streets they rumbled, jolting over the cobblestones.

The tall old houses seemed to lean together to shut out the light. The gutters were filled with dirty water. Dogs pawed among the litter in the alleys.

How different it all was from the clean, sunny little town of Arbois! Even the sharp smell of the Pasteurs' tannery was clean

Down dark and narrow streets they rumbled

compared to the foul-smelling Paris gutters.

"It will be different when we get to the Barbet School," said Jules cheerfully.

The Barbet School was in a shabby part of the city. And how closed in it was! The coach turned down a lane, and there was the school —on a dead-end street.

It was an old building. There were no trees around it.

"So this is Paris, wonderful Paris!" Louis thought. "How could one ever be happy here?"

"Louis," said Jules, when the coach had gone on and left them standing on the brick walk beside their bags, "I know what you are thinking. But this is just one part of Paris. Imagine all the sights we are going to see. Aren't you excited? Soon you will be so interested in your new studies you won't have time to be homesick."

Louis looked at his friend gratefully. "You are a good sport, Jules," he said. "I am a wretch. Yes, the studies will be wonderful. Come on!"

In a moment he was lifting the knocker on the modest front door of the Barbet School. The door opened. Clutching his bag firmly, but feeling very strange, Louis stepped into the dark hallway.

CHAPTER FIVE

Sad Days for Louis

"COME in, come in," said an old voice rather crossly. "You are late. Come this way."

The boys followed the doorman down a dark hall. A door opened suddenly before them, and they stood blinking before Monsieur Barbet.

"Welcome," the headmaster greeted them with a warm handclasp. "I have been expecting you."

He himself took the boys up to the dormitory and showed them the beds that would be theirs. Louis and Jules unstrapped their bags and unpacked their few belongings.

Each boy had a locker beside his narrow

bed. It took them but a few moments to put away their things neatly.

The big dormitory was bare, with rows of beds. Long, narrow windows looked out, not upon fair distant hills, but on dismal brick walls only a few feet away.

"Time for supper, you new lads." An older boy had come to show the newcomers down to the dining hall.

Monsieur Barbet stood at the head of a long table. He introduced the two new boys. Then everyone bowed his head as grace was said. They sat down, and at once Louis felt a sharp stab in the back of his leg.

Without making a sound he managed to pull out a long darning needle. It had been stuck in a cork and placed on his seat.

Louis saw the small boy sitting beside him stuff a napkin into his mouth to keep from laughing. The boy was not over nine, and Louis grinned. The youngster stared at him in astonishment.

"You aren't mad?" he whispered.

Louis shook his head and looked down at

his plate. He did not feel hungry. But it seemed only a moment before every other plate on the table was cleaned of every crumb.

"I say, Pasteur." A big boy next to him nudged Louis. "If you are not going to eat your dinner, may I have it? Thanks, thanks very much!" And before Louis could reply, he had swiftly exchanged plates, and was gobbling up Louis's meal.

Louis felt a little sad as he looked at the empty plate before him. "But I really did not want my supper anyway," he told himself.

"Don't let old Goulou the Pig start that," the small boy piped up. "He'll eat all your food. You're a good one; you didn't squeal when that needle stuck you. You didn't even tell on me."

Louis smiled at him. But he wanted nothing so much as to be alone. He must hide this miserable feeling. He must not show it, nor let even Jules know about it.

"I must live up to my promises to Papa and Mama," he thought. "They worked hard and made sacrifices to give me this chance. Tomorrow I'll start my studies. That will take my mind off home."

The next day Louis was given his new schoolbooks. He loved books, and as long as he could read he did not feel homesick. The boys were kept busy, and two weeks went by before either Louis or Jules could have a holiday.

"Come along, old boy," said Jules. "It will do you good to get out and see the wonders of Paris." Then he noticed how pale Louis looked. "What is the matter with you?" he asked.

"Nothing, Jules, truly," Louis answered. "I have studies to catch up on. But you go, do."

"You're homesick," said Jules. He put an arm around his friend's shoulders. "Come out with me. You'll feel better if you do."

"Oh, Jules," Louis could hide his feelings no longer, "I *am* sick for home. If only I could get a whiff of the tannery yard I feel I should be cured."

"The tannery yard!" exclaimed Jules. "What a smell to long for! Well, it's home, that's all. Won't you come with me, Louis?"

But Louis would not go. He was very unhappy. Every day, alas, he grew thinner and thinner. And the hungry Goulou next to him at table grew fatter and fatter.

"The Pasteur lad," said one of his teachers, "he looks very badly. He is pale, and has lost weight. He eats nothing, and has circles under his eyes."

"Yes," nodded Monsieur Barbet. "I know. He is trying to study, but he is homesick. I shall have to do something about it."

Not long afterwards Louis was asked to go to the headmaster's office. "Someone is waiting to see you, at the corner café," he was told.

Who could it be? Louis went wonderingly to the café. At a small table in the back of the little restaurant sat a man with bent head. His face was covered with his hands.

"Papa!" exclaimed Louis. He could scarcely believe it.

"I have come to fetch you home," said his father. "Monsieur Barbet wrote to me."

"But—but my studies?" Louis faltered, though his eyes were shining with happiness.

"You can study just as well at Arbois," his father said, "and later, you can teach there. What could be finer than that?"

[60]

And so Louis went back to Arbois. How different was the coach ride back to the Jura hills! Mama and his sisters were waiting for him at the door of the house on the Cuisance. They greeted him with open arms; and nothing was said about his leaving the Barbet School.

It was wonderful to be home again. Even going back to school in Arbois was wonderful. Louis loved it. And Monsieur Romanet was very kind. He arranged Louis's studies so that he could go right on with the class.

This was all very pleasant. But Louis felt badly because he had failed in the Barbet School. He had been sent away to Paris to learn to be a teacher. And here he was back in Arbois; all because he had grown homesick.

"I should have been stronger," he scolded himself. "I disappointed Papa and Mama, after they had saved up their money to send me to Paris. But from now on I shall do my very best."

And so, by the end of the term, Louis had won more prizes than he could carry home.

And Monsieur Romanet said to him, "Louis, why not go on with your studies at Besançon? It is an excellent college."

Jean Joseph Pasteur was much pleased when Louis told him of this idea. "Besançon is near home," he said. "Whenever I go there to sell my leather, Louis, we can see one another." Then he untied his leather work apron and went into the house to talk to Mama about it. She, too, was pleased with the idea.

"I will go to Besançon," Louis reported to Monsieur Romanet, next day. "I shall prepare there to teach science. I shall study chemistry."

Monsieur Romanet was delighted.

"And this time I'm not going to give up as I did in Paris," Louis promised himself as he hopped into bed that night. "Now I am sixteen. I shall show Papa and Mama. I will *stay* in Besançon and study."

And he blew out his candle, and fell asleep dreaming of what he would do in Besançon.

CHAPTER SIX

"I Shall Find Out Something Wonderful!"

A TALL, slender young man in a double-breasted jacket came briskly up to the front door of the old Barbet School in Paris. He was a handsome young man, and he smiled to himself as he lifted the knocker.

"There he is! There's Monsieur Pasteur," exclaimed a boy who was watching from a window.

A half-dozen pupils pressed closer to see. "He's coming in. Let's get in our seats, fellows, and be ready," said another pupil. "I don't want to miss *this* lesson."

The boys took their seats quickly. In a moment Louis came into the classroom. Yes, here he was teaching. And in the Barbet School!

[*63*]

He had graduated from Besançon with honor.

For an hour the boys listened with interest while Louis explained to them some of the wonders of science. When the class was over, a young student named Roux stopped to speak to the professor.

"Monsieur Pasteur," said young Roux, "I would like to come to your laboratory, sir, if you would let me. I am interested in chemistry. And I have never looked through a microscope." The boy's eyes shone eagerly. "It would be wonderful if I could."

"Of course you may, Roux." Louis smiled. "I'll be there. Come at four. It will be a pleasure."

Promptly at four young Roux came quietly into the laboratory. Monsieur Pasteur was absorbed in studying something through the microscope. He did not hear Roux.

The boy looked wonderingly about the badly lit room. To him it was a magic place. He did not see the unpainted plaster walls, the dingy shelves, and the rough tables.

He saw the rows and rows of jars and bottles

on the shelves—all filled with mysterious powders and liquids, white and yellow and green. Each had a name printed on a label.

There was a rusty little stove in one corner, and a sink with cold running water. As Roux waited, the door opened again and the cleaning woman came in.

Monsieur Pasteur looked up quickly. "Ah, there you are, Mrs. McGudge," he said pleasantly. "I don't believe we need any cleaning today."

"Faith, and I should hope not, sir," said Mrs. McGudge. "I'm just after cleaning this morning, sir. I washed the windys again, as you said. And the shelves. But the stove, sir—"

"No, no," said Louis hastily. "Don't bother with the stove now, if you please, Mrs. McGudge. We mustn't raise any dust." He ran his finger over the shelf and looked to see if there were any dust on it. "I shall be uncovering some slides presently," he explained. "We can't have any dust getting on them."

Mrs. McGudge wanted to shake down the ashes. Now weren't ashes clean? She shrugged her shoulders and, behind Louis's back, tapped her head. "The poor professor," she said under her breath to Roux. "He's quite daft. Crazy, lookin' through that glass all day at specks."

But now young Professor Pasteur saw Roux. "Wouldn't you like to look?" he said as he changed the slide.

The boy put his eye to the microscope.

"Wonderful!" he exclaimed. "I can see beautiful shapes—they sparkle."

"Those are crystals," Louis said, "tartaric acid crystals from grapes. Now look at this."

He changed the slide again. "Here we have some *para*tartaric acid crystals," he explained. "They, too, come from grapes. But paratartaric acid is a rare and mysterious acid. It is badly needed in making certain medicines and dyes. But the chemists do not know how to make it.

"This paratartaric acid seems to be exactly like plain tartaric acid. Yet it does not act the same way. But there *is* one important difference between the two crystals. Can you see the difference, Roux?"

Roux looked carefully through the microscope. "Yes," he said. "I see the difference. These paratartaric acid crystals are dark. They do not sparkle like the others. Why not?"

"I can't tell you why—yet," Louis replied. "But I intend to find out. And when I do, I shall have the key to one of Nature's secrets. Crystals are like building blocks—"

"Go ahead, Professor," said a voice behind them.

Louis looked up quickly. "Charles!" he exclaimed. It was an old school friend, Charles Chappuis, who had been at Besançon with him.

"I am enjoying the lecture," said Charles smilingly. "Pray go on. What doors of Nature will that crystal key unlock?"

"Ah well, you shall see, my friend," replied Louis affectionately. "I shall find out something wonderful from my crystals."

CHAPTER SEVEN

A Great Discovery

G OOD gracious, Louis," exclaimed Charles, as he came into the laboratory one day. "What are you doing with that bag of bones?"

"I'm making phosphorus," Louis replied. "Sit down, Charles." And he threw the bag off the only chair.

"It's time to go to dinner," said Charles. But he sat down to wait. He knew he could not pry Louis away from his work until he had finished.

Louis poured some white powder into a small bottle. He labeled it *phosphorus,* and set it proudly on a shelf. Then he took off his smock and reached for his coat. "Come along, Charles. What are we waiting for?"

"Food!" said Charles. "Some beef ragout, at that wonderful little restaurant in the basement. You can also get onion soup there, crescent rolls, coffee, and a cream-filled Napoléon, all for four francs."

Louis enjoyed his dinner that night. But in the days that followed he had little time to dine with Charles. He was working early and late. Not only was he teaching school. He also was going on with his studies at the Teachers Academy.

As the weeks passed Louis was usually to be found in the Academy laboratory.

"Good old Louis," his fellow students would say laughingly. "He's a laboratory pillar. If he came out of the lab it would fall down."

But when the Academy examinations came, only four students passed. And Louis was one of the top three.

"Ah, they will see what Pasteur will be," said Charles.

One warm afternoon at the end of a summer's day, the door of Professor Pasteur's laboratory opened with a bang. Young Roux, who was now an Academy student, was walking along the hall. He jumped as though a shot had been fired.

Out of the laboratory door ran Professor Pasteur. He raced wildly along the hall, and bumped into Roux. He hugged the young man in delight. "I've found it. I've found it!" shouted Pasteur.

"What have you found, Monsieur?" asked Roux in astonishment.

"The secret of the crystals!" said Louis. "Come out into the garden with me, do, and I will tell you about it."

They seated themselves on a bench and Louis looked happily at his young friend. "Do you know," Louis said, "I found that each tartaric acid crystal has a tiny face on one side. This face is like a little mirror. It reflects light to the *right*. And the crystal sparkles.

"Each *para*tartaric acid crystal has a face also. Some of these crystals reflect light to the right. But an equal number reflect light to the *left*."

"If they reflect light, why do they not sparkle?" asked Roux.

"They do!" Louis replied excitedly. "But only when I separate them. When the right-handed crystals are alone, they sparkle. And when the left-handed crystals are alone, *they* sparkle too. Do you know what that means?"

"No," replied Roux. "I don't."

Louis laughed. "Why, it means that when I find out—and I shall—how to change half of the right-handed crystals in plain tartaric acid

[72]

into left-handed crystals, I shall have discovered how to *make* the rare paratartaric acid."

The next day the head of the Academy, Monsieur Balard, heard of Louis's discovery.

"This is truly important!" he exclaimed. "By his careful study Louis has found something which no scientist has ever noticed before. I must tell Monsieur Biot. He is the most important chemist in France. Yet even he did not observe the difference between the crystals of these two acids which seem so much alike."

Monsieur Biot could not believe that a young man who had been studying only a few years could make such a discovery. How could he separate such tiny crystals, one from the other?

"I would like to see for myself what this young man claims," said Biot.

But Louis did not reply to Monsieur Biot. For now, just when he had made his first real success, Mama Etienette lay dying. By the time Louis reached home—she was gone.

Mama! How he would miss her tender love. From her he had gotten all his curiosity and enthusiasm. This was the only sorrow in the Pasteur family since they had lost little Émilie.

It was many weeks before Louis returned to Paris. Soon afterward Monsieur Biot did see for himself that Louis was right about the grape crystals.

"He is a remarkable young man," said Biot. "The world will hear of him. He is so careful that he sees what no one else can see. Furthermore, he has taught us a new way to study chemistry. There is a reason for everything in Nature, and if we look hard enough we can find it."

[74]

Back in Arbois at the house on the Cuisance Papa Pasteur was sitting reading. It was a book that Louis had sent him so that he too could study chemistry.

"Look, Papa, look," cried Josephine as she peeked out of the window. "Here comes Monsieur Romanet. And the Mayor. And Jules Vercel."

"What can they be coming for?" exclaimed Virginie. Hastily she put away the last of the supper dishes.

A few minutes later the callers were seated in the living room. The Mayor cleared his throat and wiped his forehead with a red kerchief.

"Monsieur Pasteur," he began, "it is an honor to call upon you, the father of a young man who has brought fame to Arbois. Er—ah," the Mayor grew excited. "You tell him, Monsieur Romanet."

"Ah, Monsieur Pasteur," said the schoolmaster, beaming, "we are so happy about Louis. Did I not always say he would do something important? Although he is so young he

[75]

has become famous because of his work with crystals. They say he will be one of the leading scientists of France. Regard!" Monsieur Romanet held out an important-looking letter.

"He has read a most important paper before the French Academy of Science. Our congratulations, Monsieur!"

Monsieur Romanet's eyes were moist. And indeed, Jules, Virginie, and Josephine were all weeping joyful tears.

"Louis has been a good son," said Jean Joseph, with a smile on his sad face. "That is the important thing."

Meanwhile Louis had been sent to Strasbourg to teach. He was pleased. There was a good laboratory in the Strasbourg Academy.

One day, after he had been in Strasbourg for two weeks, he stood in front of a mirror in the bedroom of his apartment, brushing his coat. He brushed his hair even more carefully. He had been invited out to dinner at the home of Monsieur Laurent, the head of the Strasbourg Academy.

As Louis hurried towards the home of Monsieur Laurent he thought of all the scientific matters which he would discuss with his host. But he forgot all about science the moment

that Monsieur Laurent's door opened, for there stood Monsieur Laurent's daughter, Marie.

What a lovely girl she was! She had great blue eyes, a sweet round face, smooth brown hair like satiny wings folded close to her head.

Louis fell in love with her at first sight. She soon learned to love him dearly. And on a beautiful day in May they were married.

Marie was a wonderful wife. Louis's work came first, she said. And she helped him in the laboratory, and wrote out his notes for him.

Louis went on happily with his work. For as he watched many kinds of crystals forming, he began to see how and why they formed. And one day, after trying many, many methods, many times, he decided to heat tartaric acid very hot, and keep it at the same heat for several hours. At the end of that time it was transformed—into paratartaric acid! Louis, by changing the form of crystals, had changed one chemical into another!

When the wonderful news was announced, Louis was given the Red Ribbon of the Legion of Honor for his discovery. And all the scientists were very much excited. Nature was always changing matter—food into bone and muscle, earth and minerals into vegetables and flowers. But for a thousand years, and maybe longer, men had been trying to transform one chemical into another. Now at last it had been done—by Louis Pasteur.

CHAPTER EIGHT

Jeanne Does Some Crystal Gazing, Too

THREE children were looking out of a front window of the Teachers Academy in Paris, where Professor Louis Pasteur and his family now lived. There was fair-haired Jeanne, who was seven. And blue-eyed Jean Baptiste, almost six. And dark-eyed Cécile, who was four. Marie Louise, the youngest, was asleep.

"Here comes Papa!" Cécile cried joyfully.

Louis looked up and saw the children waving from the window. He waved back and ran up the steps, two at a time. The children met him at the door. He kissed them all and tossed them one after the other up into the air. When

[*80*]

their squeals of joy had ended, Louis went to find his wife, Marie.

"Are you tired, Louis?" Marie asked.

"Just a little bit," Louis replied, sitting down in his big armchair.

Marie hung up his hat and coat. She shook her head as she looked at his overcoat. It was frayed and shabby.

But Louis did not think of his clothes. When he had left Strasbourg to go to Lille, as Professor of Science and Dean of the Univer-

[81]

sity, he had thought only of the opportunity to study and teach. For Lille was the center of many rich chemical factories.

His flashing enthusiasm, his sparkling eyes, had drawn many students. Lille had become a great university. And in his little laboratory there, Louis had discovered many mysteries.

He had seen little living buds growing in fermenting beer. And he had seen strange little rods in sour milk.

"Living beings are made up of chemicals," Louis had said to himself. "Do these buds cause fermentation in beer? Do the chemicals in them work changes?"

And then suddenly Louis had been called to Paris. He had been made Dean of the Teachers Academy, and now the Pasteurs lived at the school. The children were thrilled and delighted with Paris. The river in the spring, the shops on the bridges, the pointed rooftops—it was all wonderful!

And Louis was happy, too, to be back in charge now of the school where he had been a student. But his laboratory, alas! He had to make one in the attic under the roof. Everything had to be carried up three flights of stairs, but at last it was ready.

"Papa," Jeanne begged now, eagerly, "may I come upstairs tomorrow, and look at the grape crystals through the microscope? My eyes are sharp. See!" She opened her gray-green eyes until they were as round as marbles.

"But yes, my little one," replied Louis. He laughed with pleasure. "But I am now studying other acids—fermenting beer, and wine."

The next morning Jeanne went up to her father's laboratory.

"Observe, Jeanne. I shall show you something most interesting." He brought a high stool for her to sit on. Then he chose a small eight-sided crystal and with a knife broke off a piece of it. Now he put the crystal back into the liquid in which it had formed.

"Now you will see a fascinating sight, my Jeanne," he said. "Watch the crystal from time to time. You will see what we call molecules growing. Molecules are tiny clumps of matter. They are little bunches of atoms."

Jeanne put her eye to the microscope. Presently she called out, "Papa, see! Tiny little crystals are gathering all over the big crystal."

"Yes, yes!" Louis was delighted that she watched so carefully. "After lunch you shall look again."

When they looked again, the broken part had grown even more rapidly than the rest. And soon the crystal was just as it had been at first, only larger. The broken part had grown out again.

"It is wonderful!" said Jeanne. She could not take her eyes away from the microscope.

"You see, the wounds are healed," Louis said. "Almost as if they were bodily wounds, in a living being."

"It's like magic. Like a fairy tale!" Jeanne looked up with shining eyes.

"Yes," replied her father, as he lifted her down from the stool and patted her blonde hair. "Perhaps the forming of crystals is one of the steps of the beginning of life. Chemicals act like living beings often. As you have seen, they grow.

[85]

"When you go downstairs, you yourself may try an experiment," Papa added. "You may get one or two teaspoonsful of soda from the kitchen—baking soda. Put it in a cup, and fill the cup half full of water."

"What will happen?" cried Jeanne.

"Wait. Stir it well, to dissolve the soda. Then you must put the cup aside for a while—until the water has evaporated. Maybe next day, maybe two days. Then look. There will be a cake of shiny crystals in the bottom of the cup.

"And all around the sides—lovely crystal forms. Like frost on the windowpane. Sometimes you have to add a little water. Or pour some off if there is too much. Try it, my little chemist!"

"Oh, I shall, Papa!" Jeanne pulled an apple from her pocket, to eat on the stairs. "It will be wonderful to make some crystals for myself."

CHAPTER NINE

"*Unseen Giants*"

JEANNE sat once more on a high stool in her father's laboratory. One eye was held tight to the microscope. The other she covered with her fingers.

"Papa, Papa," she cried suddenly. "Come see!" She pushed her fair curls back without taking her eye from the microscope.

"You have found something, my child," exclaimed Louis with delight.

"I am looking at the little white beads of yeast. I watched them bud. They grow. Like tiny bead stems, with flowers." Jeanne looked up, her face glowing. "Observe, Papa," she cried.

LOUIS PASTEUR

Louis put his eye to the microscope. "Yes, that is a yeast germ budding. Yeast germs are good little germs. One yeast bud can raise a mountain of dough."

"Does the yeast germ keep on growing after the dough is baked into bread?" Jeanne asked curiously.

"No, the heat of the oven kills the yeast germs," Papa replied. "Look, Jeanne, here are some other germs—bad ones." Louis slipped another slide beneath the microscope.

"Oh, what a pretty blue!" Jeanne exclaimed. "Now I see some little sticks, like tiny jackstraws. They are wiggling around. They look like weenie strings of sausages!" Jeanne was so excited that she jumped off the stool.

"They are breaking off into more sticks. What are they, Papa?"

"They are called bacilli. For a long time Papa has been working to find out what makes milk turn sour. Now he has discovered that it is these little rod-shaped bacilli. Papa has colored them blue so that they will be dark

[88]

*"Papa has been working to find out
what makes milk turn sour"*

enough to see. Soon there will be hundreds of them, for each one breaks into two."

"Oh, Papa, I would know them anywhere," exclaimed Jeanne. "There are so many tiny things in that little round world under the microscope, I love to look into it. A drop of rain water is like a tiny ocean. Yesterday I looked at one and saw wee little green things swimming around and around in it."

"She will be a great chemist," cried Papa in delight. "Run out in the sun, now, and play, my child." Jeanne went off, hippety-hop, eating an apple.

Louis watched her absent-mindedly. He was thinking about the rod-shaped bacilli which he had found in milk. "Sour milk makes sick babies," he thought. "I must find a way to kill these bacilli which cause the milk to turn sour."

He went back to his laboratory table. And before he knew it, Marie was calling him to supper. His thoughts were still on his work as he sat down at the table. "Where do they come from, these germs?" he said inquiringly to his family. "We did not even know about them before we had the microscope."

"I never see any, Papa," said little Marie Louise cheerfully, and everyone laughed.

"They are so small," said Papa. "But like a magician they can change one thing into another. Unseen giants . . ."

"Where are the giants, Papa?" asked Jean Baptiste, looking over his shoulder fearfully.

"They're all around us," Jeanne teased. "But when we've found them, there will be no more sickness, will there, Papa?"

Louis shook his head. After the blessing he wiped his plate carefully with a fresh napkin. Each of the children did the same.

"I know the dishes are always clean, Marie dearest," Louis said with a smile. "But I believe that these tiny germs must live in the air, in dust we do not see. The baker could not even see all that went into his dough, or we would not find all of this."

He crumbled his bread on the tablecloth into a little pile, and separated from it—a thread, a pebble, a roach's wing.

"Papa, you always see things that no one else can see," laughed Jeanne, biting into her own little crescent roll with relish. "But you say that heat kills yeast germs, and *all* the germs in this bread are baked."

Louis looked at the little girl in astonishment. She had given him an idea. It was as plain as the nose on his face. Baking stopped bread yeast from rising and growing—and turning sour. Why wouldn't heat stop bacilli from souring milk?

For the next two days Louis was very busy in his laboratory. That night at supper he asked his family, "How do you like your milk?"

"It is good, Papa. Delicious! It seems even richer than usual," the children chorused. "Have you done something to it?"

"Have I done something to it?" laughed Louis. "I have heated it for half an hour at a temperature of 142 degrees Fahrenheit, so any little germs or bacteria would be killed. Thus the milk cannot turn sour. At least, not for some time."

"Louis, that is wonderful!" exclaimed Marie, as she filled up the milk mugs again. "You did not let the milk boil, I am sure, for the taste is not changed."

"Ah," exclaimed Louis, rubbing his hands in delight, "that is what I wanted to hear! No, the taste does not change. And the day will come when all the world will heat its milk, to keep it sweet and safe. Then we shall see how many babies are saved."

Louis spent many precious hours in the

"Ah, Marie, I might have saved our little Jeanne"

laboratory. Days, weeks, and months passed—teaching and study, teaching and study, long hours over the microscope. The months grew into years.

Jeanne was a big girl now, thirteen years old, and Jean Baptiste twelve. It was a very hot summer that year, so hot in the attic that in winter had been bitter cold.

Louis was glad that Marie was in the country with the children. But in September Marie wrote that Jeanne was ill.

"It is typhoid fever, Louis," said the letter. "And no one knows what to do for it." Louis went at once to the country, but from the beginning it was hopeless. Little Jeanne died.

"If only I had been a doctor instead of a chemist," Louis said in his grief. "I might have found out the germ that caused the typhoid. Ah, Marie, I might have saved our little Jeanne."

"Oh, Louis, where do those germs come from?" asked Marie sorrowfully.

"No one knows," Louis replied. "But not from within the body. Of this I am sure. And

I intend to prove it. I shall talk to my good friend Biot about this."

And Louis hurried off to see the great chemist.

CHAPTER TEN

What's in the Air?

Monsieur BIOT was an old man, and he loved Louis. But now he gazed in astonishment as Louis told him what he wanted to do.

"I am going to prove that germs do not spring up in the body by themselves," Louis said. "They enter the body from outside. And the body sickens, just as milk sours and food spoils, when they are left exposed."

"But how can you hope to answer the question that man has always asked—where does sickness come from?" asked the gray-haired scientist. "No one has yet been able to find an answer to this."

"Well, I shall try to find it," Louis replied firmly. "I am convinced that there is a different germ for every illness. And I believe that every germ comes from a parent germ. Do birds and dogs and men just spring up by themselves?" he asked. "No! Well, neither do the small creatures which we can see only through the microscope. All have parents."

"Ah," replied Biot, "and where does the parent come from, then?"

"From the earth, from the dust, from the air," cried Louis. "This germ life is all around us. The germ seeds, or spores, need only to fall in a place where the germs can begin to grow. And if they are in the air, then we can catch them."

Louis left Biot, more than ever determined to prove that germs were in the air.

But how should he go about proving it? First of all he would have to have a special laboratory. It would take many experiments.

"How about that little building at the corner of the Academy?" said Marie. She was knitting a little jacket for baby Camille, who was just a year old.

"Yes, I can use that!" Louis planned.

It was better than the old attic he had once used, even though he had to crawl under the staircase on his hands and knees to reach the stove. And now for the first time in his work, he had an assistant.

"Bring me all the flasks and bottles we have," he said to the boy, an Academy student. "I'll start the fire in the stove while you fetch them."

[*99*]

Louis disappeared under the staircase. When the new assistant returned, Louis had the fire started and was waiting for him. His smock was smudged, his knees dusty, and cobwebs were in his hair and beard. But on his face was a beaming smile.

"Now I am ready to begin," he cried.

And so began the experiments which were to tell the world about that other, invisible world.

Louis chose a glass tube. He plugged it with cotton. The cotton grew dark with what it caught from the air. He put the cotton in some pure water which had been boiled until the microscope showed not a single germ in it, for boiling kills both germs and their spores.

Louis watched the flask of water carefully. In a short time it was filled with many kinds of germs, or bacteria, as these tiny microscopic creatures are called.

"But," he said to himself, "these germs *might* have been in the cotton already. I have a better idea."

Now Louis had some glass flasks made, with

curved necks, like a swan's. He filled the flasks half full of water, and boiled the flasks. Air then passed upward through the long neck of each flask, and left its germs on the curve as it went on down into the flask.

Then Louis carefully tipped the flasks so that the water would wash over the curve and pick up any germs there. Now he straightened the flasks so the water was level again, and waited. Nothing had touched the flasks and the water but air.

This was an adventure into a new world! How eagerly Louis watched those flasks! Columbus could not have looked more anxiously for the new world. Early next morning Louis hurried into his laboratory, his heart pounding with excitement.

He put some water from one of the flasks on a slide under his microscope. The water was swarming with life!

"Marie, Marie!" he called in his delight. "Come, come, my dear, and see what has happened."

Marie and Cécile came running, and they

too looked at the drop of water beneath the microscope. "Louis, it is wonderful!" Marie cried.

"These germs came from the air," he explained. "They have multiplied a thousand times over, into millions of bacteria."

"How do they grow and multiply, Papa?" asked Cécile, as she put her eye to the wonderful magic window of the microscope.

"Each little one-celled creature divides in two," answered Louis. "Then these two divide also. This goes on, very swiftly, until there are millions from the first parent germ. And each germ is like its parent."

"I want to see too," cried little Marie Louise.

"Yes, yes, you shall see." Papa wanted them all to see.

News that Pasteur had found that the air was filled with germs spread quickly. But still the world would not believe it.

"If there were that many germs in the air," argued the scientists, "it would be full of loose spores floating around. Why, they would make a mist as thick as iron." And they laughed scornfully.

"Perhaps," said Louis to himself, as he paced up and down his little laboratory, "perhaps the air, like the earth, has more life in it at one place than at another."

In the days that followed Pasteur was seen going about from cellar to attic, from street to garden.

"*What* is Professor Pasteur doing?" people asked. "He goes around waving bottles and flasks as though he were crazy." Maybe he *was* a little crazy, they thought.

Louis Pasteur was collecting air. Quickly he would knock off the top of an airtight glass container; he would leave it open for an instant, then swiftly reseal it. The flasks had first been half filled with water and boiled.

The next morning Louis found bacteria in most of the flasks. But there were some flasks that had no germs at all.

So, some air was pure. "I'll go up to the Alps," Louis decided. "High mountains always have clear air. And I'll take air samples right across the country. Thus we shall learn a great deal about air-borne germs."

But before going to the Alps, Louis went to Arbois. His old friend Jules Vercel joined him there. As he and Jules jogged around the countryside in an old buggy, Louis opened twenty flasks in the fresh country air. He sealed them at once. When they were re-opened later, only eight had bacteria in them.

The workers in the vineyards of Arbois gazed at Louis in astonishment. What kind of nonsense was this?

"Imagine, the tanner's son is bottling air!" They laughed and nudged each other.

Even Jules could not take Louis seriously. "It amuses him to do it," he thought. "Why not?"

"I'd like to go up in a balloon for samples of air," said Louis. "I'd like to see how high the germs of earth are carried."

But he had no balloon and the Alps were very high, so off he and Jules went, climbing behind a mule laden with a case of the precious glass flasks.

There came a day at last when Louis Pasteur stood before a great audience at the famous University of Paris, the Sorbonne. Many people had come to hear him speak. The hall

was packed, the day was one to be remembered—April 7th, in the year 1864.

"Dear Heaven, it looks like the National Theatre!" exclaimed a fashionably dressed woman, as she took her seat. "There is the

Princess Mathilde. And Alexander Dumas, the great writer!"

"All the celebrities are here," said her companion, hoping her elegant new taffeta dress would be noticed.

"Hush! He is going to speak!"

Pasteur stood up before them. Silence filled the great hall.

"Can living creatures come into the world by themselves?" Pasteur began. "Can living things so different, so strange in their shapes, just appear—without having come from other living things?"

A murmur swept over the audience.

Pasteur held up two flasks of water for all to see. "I have here two bottles." he said. "One was prepared today. It holds boiled water which I left open to the air. Germs dropped into it. Tomorrow it will be filled with bacteria—unimaginably tiny animals and vegetables."

The audience now listened with breathless quiet. Not a sound was heard except the voice of Pasteur.

A murmur swept over the audience

"The second flask," Pasteur went on, "holds clear, pure water. It is four years old. It will always stay clear. Why? Because no air can enter it. It is sealed, airtight."

Now the great chemist held up a third bottle.

"Here I brought together pure mountain air and pure water," he said, "and there are still no germs in the flask. Because there are no parent germs there. Thus we see that bacteria do not come into being by themselves."

A wave of sound rippled over the hall. But Pasteur spoke again.

"Wherever the air and the wind carry germ spores, those germ spores will grow when they find the right food to grow in," he said clearly. "The spores remain alive, for who knows how long.

"If we put some of this germ-filled water into another liquid, soon that liquid, too, will be swarming with millions of bacteria."

Pasteur looked about the vast hall. Then he said, "So we see that life does not come into being by itself. Each germ must have a parent.

And we see, also, that germs are carried through the air."

What wild excitement and clapping of hands filled the hall! And the news of what Pasteur had discovered echoed around the world.

CHAPTER ELEVEN

Pasteur Helps the Wine Makers

LOUIS sat under the quince trees in Arbois with his father. On one side the little Cuisance River chattered over the pebbles. On the other the tannery was strangely silent. The girls were both married and away. And the tannery was idle for the time. For Louis was home on a visit.

The soft air blew down from the vineyards on the hills. It brought the scent of ripening grapes. Jean Joseph had brought out a tray of brioches, those delicious little French rolls. And some wine that he had been keeping for years.

"Ah, this wine, my son," Jean Joseph remarked, sipping it slowly, "I fear we shall have no more fine wine like this. There is a wine sickness which is traveling all over France."

"But this is delicious." Louis raised his glass. "To your health, Papa!"

"Here comes Armand Duval." Jean Joseph looked towards the bridge. "Poor Armand! He is in trouble. For two years he has not been able to sell his wine, because it has soured!"

A few moments later, Armand Duval was bowing to his old friends. His sun-browned leathery face was creased in wrinkles of worry.

"Ah, Monsieur Louis," he said, as he sat down beside Louis and his father, "I wonder if you can help us. Our beautiful wines are spoiling. We cannot sell them.

"What is the trouble, you ask? They all sicken. All, all, will be lost, if you cannot help us. And I," Armand Duval shook his head sadly, "I shall be ruined."

"Monsieur Duval," Louis said sympathetically, "I will do what I can. Have you some samples of your wine with you?"

Yes, Armand had brought several bottles of

his ailing wine. He gave them to Louis, who promised he would try to find out why the wine had spoiled.

News travels fast, and before dusk the Mayor of Arbois was also calling on Professor Pasteur.

"Ah, Monsieur Pasteur," the Mayor said, "we would be only too honored if you would allow us to fit out a laboratory for you." He wiped his moist brow with the big red kerchief he always carried. The Mayor was fat and nervous.

"Oh no, Monsieur le Maire," Louis answered, "I shall do very well in the old coffee-house at the edge of town."

When the Mayor had gone, Louis joined his father upstairs over the shop. A rosy-cheeked country girl had prepared their supper.

"The tinker can make me the funnels and pipes I will need for my experiment," Louis explained. "If I cannot find out what ails the wines, I would hate to have put the town to the expense of fitting out a laboratory."

Now Louis studied carefully all the wines which the growers of Arbois brought in to his

coffeehouse laboratory. It did not take him long to find out what was wrong with them.

"See, Papa," he said to his father one day, "here are the tiny growths, like the smallest of vegetables, which are spoiling the wines."

"How can they be kept out of the wine?" asked Jean Joseph, peering through his son's microscope.

"It is impossible to keep them out," Louis explained. "But they can be destroyed after the wine has fermented. I'll experiment to find out how this can best be done."

And Louis soon found the answer to this problem. It was quite simple. "You must heat your wine to a temperature of from 50 to 60 degrees Centigrade," he told Monsieur Duval.

"This will kill all the sour little ferments. And it will not spoil the taste of your wines."

Armand Duval could hardly speak his gratitude.

News of Louis's discovery spread throughout France. Soon all the wine makers were heating their wines, and the wines no longer soured.

"You have saved the wine industry of France, my dear Pasteur," wrote Louis's old teacher, Monsieur Dumas.

But when Louis returned home to Paris he found that France was facing an even more costly trouble. Another letter from Dumas awaited him.

"A terrible disease is killing off the silkworms," wrote Dumas from his home in Alais. "France's silk business will be ruined. Millions of dollars will be lost, if something is not done."

"Dumas wants me to try to help the silkworm growers of Alais," Louis said to Marie. "He says that thousands of silkworm growers from all over France are writing the Govern-

[*115*]

ment to send someone to Alais to study the disease."

"I hate to have you go away again," said Marie. "Yet perhaps you ought to."

"But I know nothing of silkworms," Louis replied. "I have never seen a silkworm in my life. Still I know that I would be sorry if I did not try to help."

"But come now, let us sit down to dinner." Marie rose and led the way into the dining room. "We have a wonderful feast, Louis, in your honor. The children are waiting."

"See, Papa, goose liver, roast of lamb, potato soufflé," cried Jean Baptiste, who already had his napkin tucked into his collar. Jean Baptiste was fourteen now, slender but tall.

"And for dessert," Marie Louise sang out, "may I tell him, Mama? Candied chestnuts!"

Papa asked a blessing on the food, and then the family sat down.

"Jean Baptiste," said Cécile sternly, "in dirt there are germs that one must be afraid of. True, Papa? Look at your hands and neck, my brave one."

Jean Baptiste hastily pulled up his collar and hid his hands. The little girls laughed merrily. They thought that everything Jean Baptiste did was wonderful.

"I *am* afraid of germs," he said. His honest eyes were wide and blue like his mother's. "They are not such good company." He grinned.

"Ah, my son," replied his father quickly, as he heaped the boy's plate. "Your papa does not want to frighten you. There are good bacteria as well as bad. Many of these tiny invisible creatures help us."

"If you do not like germs, Jean Baptiste, you should wash them away," said Cécile primly.

"Cécile is right," Papa agreed. "Nature is wise. She wants us to be clean. And it is chiefly in dirt that danger lies. But, after dinner, I shall tell you more about the good germs. More salad, if you please, Mama. It is perfect."

After dinner Papa sat in his armchair, and the children gathered around him. "Tell us now about the good germs," said Cécile.

[*117*]

"Ho-ho," laughed Papa. "So you will listen to your old papa tell of those little microscope people. Well, first, you must know that sunlight and air kill many bad germs. Some poison germs die instantly in air.

"And the next thing to know," he put his arm around Jean Baptiste, "is that good germs —the germs of decay—are very useful. What do they do? Well, when anything dies—trees, animals, plants—these little germs of decay light upon them. And they cause the dead plants and animals to rot away, and go back to earth to be used for new life."

"But where are those germs, Papa?" asked little Marie Louise. She had been listening as if to a fairy tale. "And can we only see them through a miker-scope?"

"Yes, that's our magic eye," said Papa. "But germs are everywhere—in the air, in the water, in the earth. And if we didn't have those germs which make things rot away, the earth would be piled so high with everything that there wouldn't be any room left."

"Well, I guess they really are useful," Jean Baptiste admitted. "But there is one thing I would like to know. Why does not everyone get sick from 'most everything he touches?"

"Because most of us keep clean. And have sunlight," answered Pasteur slowly. "But that is a good question, Jean Baptiste. And Papa has thought much about it. There must be a reason—why one person is taken sick even when he is clean, and another is not."

At this moment Marie Louise rolled off on

to the floor. She was sound asleep. Well, it was long past bedtime. As they stood up, stretching, Mama said proudly "You know, children, France has a new word now!"

"What is it?" said Jean Baptiste eagerly.

"It is *pasteurization!*" Mama looked at Papa with shining eyes. "You know it was Papa who found the way to make milk safe. Which is much more important than to keep wine from spoiling."

The next morning Louis made ready to go to Alais. "I'm going to learn all about those busy little caterpillars whose cocoons give us silk thread," he said to his children. And he kissed them all good-by.

CHAPTER TWELVE

The Worm Doctor

LOUIS had been in Alais just nine days when a telegram came. His father, Jean Joseph, was ill. Louis hurried away to the train for Arbois. What a sad journey! He was afraid that he would not arrive in time. It might be as it had been with his mother.

Alas, so it proved. This wonderful father, who had always so loved and guided him, was gone.

"Dearest Marie," Louis wrote home. "My darling father is gone. I owe everything to him. To the kindness of his heart, the brightness of his mind. My father and my mother worked so hard for their children. For me especially, as my books and schooling cost so much."

Louis left Arbois sadly. His sister, Josephine, and her husband were to stay in the old home and take over the tanning business.

But there was work ahead for Louis and no time to lose. The silkworm growers were waiting for him at Alais, and he already had much to tell them.

"Let us begin with the worm," he said, as he walked with the growers up and down between the rows of mulberry bushes, on which the silkworms fed. "It is easy to find the sick worms, is it not, Messieurs?"

"Ah, but yes," said Gaston Aubert, one of the principal growers in Alais. "They move slowly over the hatching frames. And observe, they can barely climb the twigs of the mulberry bushes."

"I have seen," Pasteur agreed, "that they are weak. Also the sick worms hold up their heads and stretch out their little hooked feet as a kitten puts out its claws. I see also," he went on, "that many worms have died without spinning any cocoons at all."

"But if the sick worm spins," said Gaston

Aubert, "the cocoon hatches a withered moth. Its feelers are broken, its wings look singed."

"Surely such a moth cannot lay good eggs, or seed, as you call it," said Pasteur. "The moth has caught the sickness from the worm, and will pass on the sickness to her seed, I feel sure."

"Yes, I think that is right," said one of the growers. "And when healthy worms feed on bushes where sick ones have fed before, they, too, get sick."

"Well, what are we to do about it?" asked the spokesman for a number of growers. "We have tried everything, smoking out the worms, even spraying them," he added desperately.

"I have examined worms, and moths, under the microscope, and all are peppered with tiny spots," said Pasteur. "We must get rid of this disease."

"Nothing can cure it," one man declared.

"And the Government sends us a man who doesn't even know the first thing about silkworms," said another, turning away.

"Have patience," Louis replied. "This will

take some time. I do not think you have any good seed left."

"Then what do you propose to do?" asked Gaston Aubert.

"There is only one remedy," Pasteur replied. "If we are to wipe out this sickness, we must destroy all the sick worms, all the sick moths, and all their seed. The mulberry trees on which they feed must be sprayed. Then we must start with new, healthy seed. It will take time—one, two years. But the sickness must first be wiped out."

"Our industry will also be wiped out!" cried Gaston Aubert. He had no faith in what Pasteur was doing.

The growers were angry and desperate. They wrote to the Government. "Why do you send us a mere chemist like Pasteur? We need an experienced silkworm cultivator, or a man who knows something about disease in the animal world."

"Wait until spring," Dumas wrote back. He was now Senator for Alais. "If Pasteur cannot help you, no one can."

Now Pasteur began to look for some healthy moths. He studied hundreds of moths under the microscope. At last he found two healthy pairs, only two. And finally five more pairs were sent in from a neighboring town.

"Now, we shall keep these moths carefully apart," said Louis, "and we shall save their seed. When it hatches next spring, you will have healthy worms. Until then we can do nothing."

Louis bade the growers good-by, and promised to return in the spring. He hurried back to Paris. But Marie met him with a sad face.

Little Camille—their two-year-old baby—was sick. Night after night Louis watched over her. But he could not discover what caused her sickness.

All through the summer Camille was ill. And in September she died. It was just four months after Louis's father's death.

"How I wish that I were a doctor instead of a chemist," Louis said sadly to Marie.

"But you have already been of great help to the doctors," said Marie comfortingly. "Dr.

Lister of London has written you. He tells how many patients have been saved since the doctors and nurses in hospitals began to follow your ideas about killing germs. Now they scrub, and bake, and boil everything that touches a patient."

But Louis was sad, and very tired. Yet he could not rest. There was still so much work to be done. And the only way to be sure of success was to do the work himself.

As spring drew near he made ready to return to Alais. Would the new silkworm seed hatch out healthy little caterpillars? Or would the pepper disease still lie hidden somewhere, tiny and invisible—even to his microscope? A few weeks would tell whether he was right.

He reached Alais just as the seed was beginning to hatch. The tiny worms crawled out as lively as kittens. There was no pepper disease in the seed hatched at Alais that spring.

"Monsieur Pasteur was right," said Gaston Aubert to the silkworm growers who flocked to his farm. "Monsieur, from the bottom of my heart, I thank you!" Monsieur Aubert for-

*The tiny worms crawled out
as lively as kittens*

got all he had said about Pasteur. He shook his hand now and embraced him.

"In another year there will be plenty of healthy seed for everyone," Pasteur promised.

The growers could hardly believe it. "Pasteur has saved the silk industry for France!" they cried.

CHAPTER THIRTEEN

Louis Visits the Empress Eugénie

Here is a beautiful big envelope, Papa," cried Cécile. "It has the lilies of France on the seal. Oh, what can it be?"

"It's an invitation," said Marie Louise. "Papa is going to see the Emperor! Yes, look, Papa."

And Marie Louise was right! Papa smiled in surprise as he read the letter. "It is an invitation from the Emperor Napoleon III to spend a week, as his guest—at the Palace of Compiègne."

"Oh, you must go, Louis," said Mama Marie quickly.

"Yes, I shall have to go," Louis agreed. "But how can I spare the time?"

"Oh, Papa," both little girls spoke together, "do go! When you come home you can tell us about the Empress Eugénie."

And so Louis went. It was altogether a magnificent affair to which the son of the tanner of Arbois had been invited. Famous painters and writers and actors were there. And noble lords and ladies. Also a great physician—and the great Pasteur.

The entertainment began with a grand reception. Everyone was splendidly dressed. The men wore elegant tight-fitting trousers, with fancy embroidered vests and flaring coats. The ladies' hoop skirts floated and swayed. They were trimmed with lace, flowers, and ribbons.

But Pasteur wore a plain dark suit.

"You have heard of Pasteur, of course," whispered the elegant ladies behind their fans. "He is the one who discovered that the air is full of those tiny creatures, germs."

"Dear Heaven, how unpleasant!" The ladies laughed. They did not want to know about such things. Life was quite delightful, at the moment, just as it was.

[131]

*Soon the Emperor beckoned Pasteur aside
to talk to him*

Soon the Emperor beckoned Pasteur aside to talk to him.

"What led you to this amazing discovery, of living germs in the air, Monsieur Pasteur?" asked the Emperor Napoleon.

"Sire, it began with crystals," Louis replied. "Hunting for them led to finding living growths in wines, and to germs in milk. And so to germs in animals."

All the other guests were whispering. The Emperor had picked out Pasteur for a private

talk. And then the Empress Eugénie herself sent word that she, too, wished to talk to Monsieur Pasteur.

"I must remember just what Empress Eugénie looks like," Louis said to himself.

[*133*]

"So that I can tell Cécile and Marie Louise."

The Empress was very beautiful. Her smile was like the sun coming out. She led the way into the banquet hall, and Pasteur was seated at her side. Silver and crystal sparkled on the candlelit table. And such food—roast pheasant and guinea hens on sliced puffballs, truffles, and pastries.

But Louis scarcely noticed what he ate. He was thinking, "I must send to Paris at once for my microscope. Then Their Majesties can see exactly what I am talking about."

The next morning an exciting stag hunt was held. In the evening a torchlight procession wound through the gardens. Each day there was a fresh entertainment—plays and magicians' shows and puppets.

But Pasteur stayed in his rooms. He was turning his elegant apartment into a laboratory. His microscope had come.

The next day Pasteur showed the Empress and the Emperor Napoleon that wonderful invisible world which could be seen through the microscope. The Empress was delighted.

She carried the microscope down to show to her guests at tea as though it were a new toy.

"You should make a fortune from your wonderful discoveries, Monsieur Pasteur," said Napoleon. "All the world will be helped by them. They could be patented. And then you could charge for your services."

"Ah, but then I could not help science, Your Majesty," Louis smiled. "I would have to go into business. And business takes all one's time. There are many important things still to be done for mankind."

"What do you need to help you in your work, Monsieur?" asked the Emperor earnestly.

"A laboratory, Sire," replied Louis boldly. "Properly equipped."

"Monsieur," replied the Emperor, "we shall see what we can do for you."

Was it a promise? What did it mean? Louis hoped that the Emperor meant that he would provide him with a new and well-equipped laboratory.

Louis went back to Alais to continue his

work with silkworms and moths. But this was to be a sad year indeed for the Pasteur family. On the way to Alais to visit him, twelve-year-old Cécile fell ill. It was typhoid fever again!

Louis hurried to the town of Chambéry where Marie had stopped with the girls. Cécile seemed to have passed the worst. Her sweet face smiled up at him wistfully. But a few days later she grew worse. And Cécile, too, died.

"Ah, the terrible typhoid!" Marie wept. "Why do the doctors not find what causes it? Only then will they be able to cure it."

"Three little girls and my father," Louis said sadly. "All laid to rest in Arbois. Now Jean Baptiste and Marie Louise are all that is left to us."

But Time is kind and makes all sorrow easier to bear. Louis had much to think about, too, for at last work had begun on a splendid laboratory which the Emperor had given him.

Then suddenly Louis was taken ill. The sorrow and hard work of the years had been too much. His left side was partly paralyzed.

"But Monsieur Pasteur is so young still, and so brilliant! He must not die!" exclaimed the

students and the fellow scientists who loved
him.

In the first days after the worst of his illness
had passed, Louis would ask his daughter,

"How is the work on the laboratory getting on?"

He was so weak that Marie Louise did not
dare to tell him that no work at all had been
done since he fell ill, for fear of disturbing
him. And so she would go to the window and
look out, and say, "Oh, very nicely, Papa."

An officer had come from the Emperor himself

At last one morning Louis awoke with a clear head. He lay for a time listening. Then he said to his daughter, "Marie Louise, my child, I do not hear the hammering and the noises of the workmen. Have they stopped work on my new laboratory?"

"But no, Papa," replied the little girl, "they are just doing other things. They do not want to disturb you."

"They think I shall die," said Louis. "And so there is no use to build the laboratory. For no one will carry on the work of Pasteur." Tears gathered in his eyes.

Marie Louise kissed her father softly on the brow and went quietly from the room. She must tell someone. Papa was grieving.

Outside she found an officer who had come in the royal coach from the Emperor himself, to inquire about Papa. Marie Louise told him what was happening.

Early the next morning there was the sound of hammering and the creak of wheelbarrows. The noise of building was heard again. And Louis Pasteur began to get well.

CHAPTER FOURTEEN

A Silk Gown for the Empress

AH, THE Emperor does truly wish to be of help to you, my Louis," said Marie one morning. "Regard, he offers to lend us a house in Italy—a villa on the Royal Estate. There you can get well, in the country air."

"Yes," Louis smiled, "I shall take silkworms and moths and their seed with me and finish my study of them there."

And a few weeks later, the Pasteurs were settled at the Villa Vicentina, near Trieste. One morning Louis sat in the garden, under the soft blue skies of Italy, with a blanket over his knees. Marie sat beside him, writing out his notes.

"Papa, Papa!" cried Marie Louise, running out into the garden. "My silkworm seeds have hatched! My very own! And the little worms are most lively. They already climb up the mulberry leaves, and they eat."

"It is the good seed from Alais," Papa said, smiling. "The healthy moths, they laid good seed, as I felt sure they would." At once he began to feel better.

"Now we shall watch them grow," he said happily. "In a few weeks, chérie, they will be several thousand times their size now. You will be a true silkworm grower, my child."

He chuckled. "So bright, so pretty, our little daughter, eh, Marie?" he said to his wife. "And just think, she is only twelve years old."

Marie Louise had run off to the laboratory in the hatching shed. In a box on the shelf was a worm on a mulberry leaf. It had been brought in by an Italian grower. He had bought the silkworm seed from Toni, the gardener of Villa Vicentina. And he wanted to know if the worm was healthy.

Marie Louise took the worm, leaf and all,

[*141*]

from its box. "It looks rather tired," she thought. She picked up the worm with a pair of tweezers and placed it under the microscope.

What was this? A dark spot! The worm was sick! She must tell Papa!

As she opened the door into the shed she heard voices. She saw some Italian growers who had come to buy silkworm seed. Toni, the gardener, was talking to them.

"We can let you have plenty of seed," he was saying.

Now Toni took a packet of Papa's seed from the shelf. He added to it from a box that was under the counter. This was not the good seed from Alais, Marie Louise was sure. And Toni's seed was sick! She had just looked at the worm hatched from some of his stock.

Papa would be upset, but she must tell him. She slipped out the back door of the laboratory, and ran around to the garden.

Papa listened carefully. His eyes flashed. He was very angry—and Papa was almost never angry.

[142]

"This is terrible!" he cried. "Those poor growers who bought the seed trusted me. Why, all our work will go for nothing if bad seed starts the disease among the silkworms again."

Papa tried to rise from his chair. "Send for that rascal at once. We must get all that seed back. We cannot take chances."

Toni came unwillingly. "It was my own seed," he growled. "I have the right to sell it. If some was sick, they could burn the worms."

"What?" cried Louis, "you would ruin the silk farms of your own countrymen by starting the disease again? All for a few dollars! You

[143]

must get all that seed back. And never show your face here again!"

When Toni had gone Louis drew Marie Louise to him. "You are a wonderful child," he said. "How fortunate that you found that the worm which had hatched from Toni's seed was sick. You must watch your own little caterpillars very carefully now."

Every day after that, week after week, Marie Louise watched the hungry little worms eat and grow, and eat and grow. They were so active that she knew they were healthy. Finally they began to spin their cocoons. Round and round and round, the little spinners wove the silken fairy thread. At last they lay asleep, sealed in their pale golden mantles.

"These mantles will some day make a lovely silk dress," said Marie Louise. She picked a cocoon up gently and hurried into the garden to show Papa and Mama.

"My first cocoon!" She held it tenderly in her palm. "Perhaps—perhaps the thread from this could be woven into a gown for Empress Eugénie, Papa, couldn't it?" she asked.

"That is a wonderful idea." Mama nodded. "Would you like to send your silk to the Empress, chérie?"

"I would love it," cried Marie Louise. "She is so beautiful. That is what I shall do."

CHAPTER FIFTEEN

Danger in the Dust

A SHEPHERD lad was herding his flock along a country road. It was in the fertile French province of Ste. Germaine. The day was fair, the fields were richly green—but the sheep were sick.

"Where are you taking them, François?" It was old Robert who had stopped to speak to the boy. The old one, too, was a shepherd. But no sheep followed him. He had only his crook in hand.

"To the high pasture." François nodded ahead. "They seem to sicken in the pasture where we have had them."

"Don't go to the high pasture," the old peasant said sadly. "Sheep are dying there too.

[146]

The road is strewn with dead and dying sheep. It is a terrible thing, this splenic fever."

The boy stood still. He did not know what to do. "But they are dying back where I came from," he said.

"They are dying all over France," said Robert. "And so are the cattle. They droop, they gasp, their limbs shake. They say it is so in Russia and Germany too."

"What is to be done?" asked the boy. He looked fearfully over his flock.

"There is just one person who can help us," said the old man. "And that is Monsieur Pasteur—Louis Pasteur. I am going into the town now, to see the Mayor about it. I will offer my sheep for experiment. The Mayor will beg Monsieur Pasteur to come. If anything can be done, Pasteur will do it."

The old man plodded on. "First the war, and now this," he was saying as he left François standing there.

François was praying that his flock would not all die of this splenic fever. He had been tending his father's sheep ever since he was five. And he was fifteen now. He knew a great deal about sheep and he had noticed many curious things about this fever. He would tell Monsieur Pasteur about them if he could.

"If something is not done," the boy said aloud, "all will be ruined. Yes, what the war did not take, the plague will."

For France had been through a fearful war. Pasteur's son, Jean Baptiste, had fought in the war, and had returned home safely. Now he was in the Foreign Service in Denmark. Marie

Louise was grown up and married. Her little son Jacques was eight years old. And now Pasteur once more worked tirelessly in his Paris laboratory.

So it was only a few days after Robert and François met that Louis stood with them beside a fold of ailing sheep.

"Sometimes the sheep die before the shepherd has time to notice that they are even drooping," said the boy.

"Ah, Monsieur, the greenest pastures are cursed." Old Robert crossed himself. "Yonder," he pointed, "the earth is so rich that it is full of earthworms. Yet sheep keep dying there."

"Take me there," Louis said. He followed old Robert and the boy. Presently they were climbing over a low stone wall.

Yes, it was a rich field. The little burrows of the earthworms dotted it.

"Six sheep died here last year," said Robert, "and I buried them where they lay."

Louis dug up some of the worms. Then he went back to the sheepfold with Robert and took a sample of a dead sheep's spleen. He went away then, but promised to return soon.

Back in his Paris laboratory Louis found the germ spores of the anthrax bacilli which were killing the sheep. They were in both the earthworms and the spleen. He grew jars and jars of the deadly anthrax bacilli. Then he made a serum from them.

The next step was to vaccinate all animals, sick and well, with this serum. He took it back to Ste. Germaine, and tried to explain to the farmers what vaccination was.

"I discovered it by chance when I gave a chicken some weak cholera serum," he said. "The chicken did not notice it. I gave it a stronger dose, then a still stronger one, enough to have killed it. But the chicken remained perfectly well. Now I shall do the same with the sheep. First a weak dose of the vaccine, then a strong one."

"Ridiculous!" said the doctors of Ste. Germaine when they heard what Pasteur planned to do. "This fellow Pasteur, he may be a good chemist, but what can he possibly know about medicine? He is not even a horse doctor. The animals will die."

"They will not die," declared Pasteur. "The body gets used to the germs in the vaccine."

[151]

"How can he save the animals by dosing them with the very germ that made them sick?" asked the frightened farmers.

But Pasteur went right ahead, making ready to vaccinate the sheep.

"All France is waiting to see what will happen," said Roux. This young man who had been Pasteur's student in the Barbet School was now his chief helper. "Our enemies are hoping that you won't succeed. So that *they* will be right, and Pasteur will be proven wrong."

"We will show them," replied Pasteur grimly. He set up a little laboratory in a sheep shed on a farm near Ste. Germaine.

"Master, we have been given sixty healthy animals to experiment on," Roux said one day.

"Fine!" exclaimed Pasteur. "Put twenty-five sheep in one sheepfold. Put twenty-five in a second fold. The remaining ten sheep, put in a third pen by themselves."

Then, with the farmers watching, Pasteur vaccinated each of the first twenty-five sheep with a mild dose of the anthrax serum. But he did not vaccinate the twenty-five sheep in the second fold, or the ten sheep in the third pen.

"In twelve days," Pasteur told the sheepmen, "I will give each of the sheep in the second fold a strong and deadly dose of anthrax vaccine. They will all die because they have not been vaccinated. I will give each of the sheep in the first pen a dose of the same strong and deadly serum. They will live because they have been vaccinated. They will be as healthy as the ten sheep in the third pen which have not received any serum at all."

When the twelve days had passed, doctors, farmers, senators, shepherds, townsfolk, arrived from near and far. They crowded around the sheepfolds. Old Robert and the boy François were there too. Was Pasteur right about this business of vaccination? What would happen now to the sheep?

"Remember," said Pasteur, "when I give this deadly serum to the sheep in the first two sheepfolds, all those *which have not been vaccinated* will die."

[*153*]

To make sure of the test, Pasteur gave the two groups of animals in the first and second sheepfolds a triple dose of the deadly serum.

Two days later, on June 2nd, in the year 1882, at nightfall, all the sheep which had not been given the first dose of mild serum were dead. But the sheep which *had* been vaccinated were alive and well and grazing happily.

"It is astounding," everyone said. "Wonderful! Pasteur was right."

"Now, if sheep sicken, will such a dose save them?" asked old Robert, who had come up with François to thank Pasteur and to shake his hand.

"It will," said Pasteur, "if you do not wait too long. But we shall give them all a dose now so that they will not become sick."

Old Robert scratched his head. He did not quite understand.

"One thing more." Louis laid a hand on the

old man's shoulder. "There is *danger in the dust* and in the *dirt*. You must not bury the sheep which have died of the splenic fever, which we call anthrax, in your pastures.

"And you must not let sheep graze in pastures where dead sheep are buried. You must wait several years. For the anthrax germs will live in the ground all winter, and come up with the grass in the spring. And the sheep that graze there will die."

Now the farmers of France were filled with hope and joy. All Europe heard of the anthrax cure. It would save thousands of animals and millions of dollars.

Pasteur was honored for his discoveries and given beautiful medals. The most beautiful was a little silver branch with gold cocoons on it, which was presented to him by the silk growers.

One day Pasteur said to Roux, "If I can make a vaccine which will cure sheep, why can I not make a vaccine to cure the bite of a mad dog?"

"It would be wonderful," replied Roux.

"Every year more and more people are bitten by mad dogs, and most of them die."

"There are a hundred thousand dogs in Paris alone," Pasteur said thoughtfully, "and there are millions all over Europe. If this mad sickness should spread among the dogs and wolves as anthrax did among the cattle and sheep, it would be terrible. Yes, I must start working on this right now."

CHAPTER SIXTEEN

Pasteur Tries His Greatest Experiment

W E CANNOT find the germ of this bacteria that makes dogs mad," said Louis wearily as he rose from his stool. He covered the microscope carefully. The fine Paris laboratory which the Emperor had furnished him was spotless.

Marie and her grandson, Jacques, had come down to the laboratory to take Grandpapa home to dinner.

"We know that every sickness has its special microbe," said Louis, rubbing his tired eyes. "But some are too tiny to be seen—even under the microscope."

"If you cannot see them, Grandpapa," said

the little boy anxiously, "no one can, my mama says."

"No, there are some bacteria so small that even my eye cannot find them, my child," said Louis. "But we know they must be there, because of the terrible sickness that they cause."

He took the child's hand and walked towards the house.

That night after dinner Louis's old friend, Monsieur Balard, and Roux came to visit. They asked Pasteur if he had found a cure yet for the bite of a mad dog.

"No, I have found nothing yet," Louis said unhappily. "But I must, I shall."

His mind went back to that time so long ago when the mad wolf had come into Arbois. "Eight people were bitten," he recalled, "and seven died. Among them my little schoolmate. I've always wanted to find a cure. But even today the only known cure is to burn the poison out. And that must be done at once, and is not at all sure."

"Come now." Marie bustled in with a tray of sweet cakes and demitasses, tiny cups of black coffee. "Let us take our mind off this for the time. The way will be found."

"Yet it is strange," Monsieur Balard had to say as he sipped the coffee, "that this madness should be brought to many by the pet he loves most. The dog—called man's best friend."

"Ah, he is driven out of his mind, the poor dog!" said Pasteur. "He cannot help it when he gets that dreadful disease—rabies. It is not his fault when he bites a man and gives *him* rabies. And I feel sure that there is a cure for rabies if only I can find it."

Weeks passed by and still Pasteur worked and thought, and worked and thought, trying to cure both a mad dog and his bite.

At last one afternoon Pasteur appeared suddenly in the doorway of his laboratory. He was smiling and his eyes sparkled.

"Jacques, Jacques," he called. "Let us go down to the corner for some chocolate, eh?"

Jacques was on the lawn, trying to teach the French poodle to jump through his hoop.

"Grandpère," he shouted now, "you must have found a way to make the cure." He ran

[160]

across the grass and took his grandfather's hand. "I am glad, for this is the last day of my visit with you."

"Yes," said his grandfather as they walked along, "I have made a serum. We have proved in the laboratory that it will work. Already we have saved many dogs that had rabies. Come now, here is the candy shop."

But Pasteur did not stop his experiments on mad dogs. He wanted to be absolutely sure that he had found a cure. The Government let him use the old stables in the riding park at Villeneuve L'Étang, outside Paris, for his experiments. Though he had men working with him, he checked every experiment himself.

"I must leave nothing to chance," he said to Marie.

Towards spring he wrote to his son, Jean Baptiste, "Although I have treated dogs for rabies, I have not dared yet to treat human beings, but the time is not far off."

Then, suddenly, unexpectedly, the time came. It was on a Monday, the sixth of July, in the year 1885. A woman came to Pasteur's laboratory, leading a little boy.

The child hung back. He could hardly walk. Pasteur never allowed visitors, but when he saw the little boy he hurried forward. He saw at once that the child had been badly bitten.

"We are from Alsace, Monsieur," said the woman. "My little boy, Joseph, has been bitten by a mad dog. It was two days ago. The dog leaped upon him—he was going to school. He is only nine years old." The woman began to weep.

"Let us look at him." Pasteur lifted little Joseph Meister to a table. His hands were gentle.

"Regard, Monsieur Pasteur," cried Joseph's mother. "He has been bitten in fourteen places. Not on his face, for that he covered with his hands."

"What must I do?" Pasteur asked himself. "Dare I give this child the serum which has cured so many dogs?"

He called a servant and asked him to take Joseph and his mother to a comfortable room near by to rest. He told them to come back to the laboratory at five o'clock.

"I will consult Monsieur Vulpian," he said. "He is a member of the Rabies Committee, which is trying to wipe out this sickness. And I will also talk with Dr. Grancher, who has helped me here in the laboratory."

At five o'clock Vulpian, Grancher, and Pasteur examined the boy.

"Some of the bites are very deep," said Vulpian. "Why not try the treatment?"

"Yes. It is too late to burn out the wounds," agreed Grancher. "And there is no other treatment known—except yours. Let us give the boy the first inoculation at once."

[*163*]

"An inoculation?" asked the boy fearfully.

"That only means giving you a cure for the poison, my child," Pasteur said soothingly.

Joseph cried out when he saw the doctor's

needle. But it was all over in a moment. Just a prick in the arm—that was all there was to it. And he stopped crying when Monsieur Pasteur gave him some chocolate.

Now little Joseph was to stay right in the Pasteurs' home. And how carefully he was watched! Pasteur knew to the day and hour when the serum would complete the cure of an animal which had been bitten by a mad dog. But he did not know what its effect would be on a human being.

In a few days Joseph's wounds were healed. And the boy was quite happy playing with the white mice and the rabbits which the kind Monsieur Pasteur had given him. Each day Pasteur gave Joseph another dose of the serum. Each day the dose was stronger. And each day Pasteur grew more worried.

"But see, the lad runs and plays," said Marie as she watched Joseph from a window.

"If he keeps well for the next three weeks, I think we shall be safe," said Pasteur.

Yet Pasteur feared these last doses. Many times he had cured a bitten dog, but—this was a child! As the day drew near for the last inoculation he could not sleep. Hope, then fear, often kept him awake at night.

"All Paris is watching," he thought. "All

over the world people will hear about this. But what will they hear? That the little Meister boy has died? That there is still no cure for the bite of a mad dog?"

On July 15th, Joseph seemed restless. He was not feverish, but he had a crying spell. Pasteur was sick with fear. Was this the beginning of rabies?

"But regard, he is all right now," Marie comforted her Louis. "See, he eats well."

And Joseph slept soundly that night. But Pasteur did not sleep soundly. He had terrible dreams of little Meister dying in agony of rabies, as so many others had.

It was the day when the last dose of serum was to be given—July 16th. Joseph was running happily around at play. "Dear Monsieur Pasteur," he cried, when Pasteur gave him the last inoculation. "I love you." The little boy kissed Pasteur good night and went cheerfully off to bed.

Joseph slept like an angel.

But Pasteur paced the laboratory. "Twelve treatments in ten days," he muttered, "and the last one of deadly strength." He sank into a chair, his head in his hands.

"I could not be wrong. I could not be mistaken after all the tests," he said over and over.

"Ah, Louis, you have always been so careful," Marie comforted him. "And the child has shown no sign of sickness. Come now, to rest."

But through the long, dark hours of night Pasteur lay awake, fearing that Joseph would die.

Throughout all France many others were asking the question: Will little Joseph Meister really live?

CHAPTER SEVENTEEN

The Boy Who Did Not Die

THE treatment was over. Little Joseph was in good hands, and Pasteur could do nothing more for him now. He could only wait, hoping that the child was cured.

Since he was greatly in need of rest, Pasteur went to Burgundy to stay with his daughter, Marie Louise. At any minute he expected a telegram from Dr. Grancher, with news of Joseph Meister. Or a letter. But the days passed, and no word came.

Then, thirty-one days after the lad had been bitten, a letter came.

"Open it, open it, Marie Louise, my dear," said Pasteur. "Read it to me." He was afraid to read it himself.

"But Papa," cried Marie Louise. "It is wonderful news! From Roux! Joseph is in the best of health!"

A few days later came a letter from Dr. Grancher. "My dear Pasteur," he wrote, "Joseph Meister is the first human being ever to be saved from the bite of a mad dog, other than by the cruel method of burning. This will be forever famous in medical history."

What a relief! What a joy! Now Pasteur could really rest. But soon he returned to Paris. For many people who had been bitten by mad dogs were flocking to his laboratory.

They came by ones and twos. They came by sixes and sevens. A group of nineteen Russians came. They had been chewed by a great mad wolf almost two weeks before. Yet sixteen of these Russians were saved by Pasteur's treatment, late as they were in coming.

And so, in November, 1888, the Pasteur Institute was founded at Villeneuve l'Étang by the grateful people of France. Many doctors and scientists now said that Pasteur had changed the whole practice of medicine.

But there were many who still did not believe in him. "Illness comes from within the

body," such doctors still insisted. "Germs?
From outside the body? Pah!"

But Pasteur was getting old, and he no
longer tried to answer them as he had in days

[*171*]

gone by. As the years passed he worked quietly. On a beautiful summer afternoon Louis and Marie sat together on a bench in the lovely grounds of the Pasteur Institute at Villeneuve l'Étang. Louis had been very ill. Now he rested, thinking, remembering.

"It has been a good life, Marie." He took her hand in his.

"Yes." Marie smiled. "Our son, our daughter, happily married. Young Jacques in college."

"And the little ones yonder," Louis nodded to the summerhouse across the lawn. Two children played there, a boy of ten, a girl of nine. Blind man's buff, hide and seek.

"They have a much better chance to live than our children did, is it not so, Marie?" Louis said, thinking of his own little girls.

As they talked, two men came walking towards them beneath the pines and purple beeches.

"It is Roux and Grancher," said Louis.

"Good day, good day, dear Master," Roux greeted Louis affectionately. "We have good news for you. Gifts of money are pouring in to help us carry on our work."

"And doctors come from abroad," said Grancher, beaming, "to study our methods of preventing disease. Now that you have taught them, Monsieur, how to use the microscope, they are finding the germs of many diseases— of diphtheria, cholera, typhoid."

"Ah, typhoid. At last!" exclaimed Louis. "Science marches on."

"And the hospitals," continued Dr. Grancher, "if you could see them now! Thousands of lives are being saved by what you have taught the doctors. Perfect cleanliness, all instruments boiled, wounds kept covered."

"After the war," Louis remembered, "more soldiers died from infections than died on the battlefield. After operations they died like flies—until surgeons began to scrub their hands, bake the bandages, and boil the sponges."

"And the babies?" asked Marie. She wanted to hear them tell again what her Louis had done for children.

"Why, Madame," said Roux, "since milk has been pasteurized, many little ones have lived where before, many babies died."

When Roux and Grancher had gone, Louis sat, just dreaming. He was old, he was tired. His hair and beard were gray. The sound of children's voices came to him. The children themselves ran up to his bench.

"Grandpère," they begged as they sat in the sun at his feet, "tell us of the interesting things you have done. We will stand on our heads for you."

"Ah-hah," Louis laughed gently, his eyes sparkling still. "Your mama has been telling you tales. Maybe your grandmother will tell you some more."

"Very well, my little cabbages," said Marie. "It all began with crystals. How your grandfather did love his crystals! And because of them, he found that tiny vegetables, which you can see only under the microscope, were souring France's lovely wine.

"So," she went on, "Grandpère showed them how to cure the wine. Then he found out how to get rid of the silkworm diseases. Your mama knows all about that."

"It was nothing," Pasteur waved his hand, "just a matter of detective work."

"Well," said Marie firmly, "it saved France a great deal of money, and made the silkworm growers rich, and the Emperor, too."

"And what else? What else did my grandpère do?" cried the boy. He sat on the grass, hugging his knees and rocking back and forth. The little girl sat beside him, weaving daisy chains.

[*175*]

"Well, even more wonderful than curing the wine was pasteurizing milk—you know all about that, of course. Mama does it at home. But dairies are beginning also to pasteurize their milk." Marie looked at Louis tenderly.

"Then came the anthrax disease," she went on. "All the sheep and cattle were dying. But your grandpapa found the germs of that disease. And so he was able to cure it, too."

"And now, the story of Joseph Meister," said the boy eagerly. "He was a boy just like me, wasn't he, Grandmother?"

"Yes," said Louis, opening his eyes. "Like you, my boy. I worked for a long time to find a way to cure the bite of the mad dog. And then little Meister came.

"And because of him, all this came to be." He waved his hand towards the park and the buildings and the laboratories. He smiled at the children. Then he rose slowly from his bench. Leaning on Marie, he went into the house.

The summer days passed. Fall came, fall of the year 1895. The leaves of the purple beech

Louis sat, just dreaming

drifted down like flowers. Louis no longer could sit in the park now. He lay in his bed and dreamed of other days. He dreamed he was sitting once more under the quince trees, beside the Cuisance. He thought of Arbois as he had last seen it, early in the summer.

A mist had lain over the Jura hills then. Just as it had so long ago on the day he left Arbois for the first time to go to Paris.

"Louis!" A soft voice spoke. He opened his eyes. It was his Marie, her eyes as blue as cornflowers.

"Stay with me," he said. "Dearest Marie. I could have done nothing, I could not have lived, without you."

"Here is Monsieur Roux." She smiled. "You said you wanted to see him. And the new student who is so bright."

At once Louis opened his eyes wide. "Of course," he said in a bright, clear voice. "Come in, Roux, do."

"My dear Master," said Roux, "here is the student of whom I spoke to you."

Louis smiled at the young man. "Where are

[*178*]

you in your studies? What are you doing? You know, it is necessary to work." Louis closed his eyes for a moment. Then he looked at his visitors again.

"You know," he said, "Nature is helping us. Though we are attacked by germs, there are soldiers in our blood. They fight the germs. They surround and destroy them. And with our serums to help—there will be victory at last."

Louis lay quietly now in his bed. He held Marie's hand close. His thoughts went back to Strasbourg. And yet further back—to the tannery by the bridge.

And he seemed to hear his father say once more: "Louis, my son, come straight home after school."

Born at Dôle, France,
December 27, 1822

Is graduated from the College of Besançon,
to devote his life to science, 1842

Makes his first important discovery while
working with tartaric acid crystals, 1848

Learns what causes milk to spoil,
and how to prevent it, 1857

Dies near St. Cloud, France,
September 28, 1895

Opens the Pasteur Institute for the treatment
of hydrophobia, 1888